F-18
Hornet

 in detail & scale

Don Linn

TAB BOOKS Inc.

Blue Ridge Summit, PA 17294

Airlife Publishing Ltd.

England

This book is a product of Detail & Scale, Inc., which has sole responsibility for the contents and layout. Published and distributed in the United States by TAB BOOKS Inc., and in Great Britain and Europe by Airlife Publishing Ltd.

CONTRIBUTORS:

Bert Kinzey
Barry Roop
Ed Yarbrough
Paul Kopcynski
D.F. Brown

Phillip Huston
Greg L. Marshall
D. ''Buzz'' Lockwood
Luigi Perinetti
Tom Chee

In addition to the contributors listed above, the author wishes to extend special thanks to the following people and organizations for their assistance in the preparation of this book. LTC. Pete Field, USMC, F/A-18 Program Manager and test pilot, LCDR Ken Cockrell, USN, F/A-18 test pilot, Mr. William M. Frierson, Jr., Public Affairs Officer, NAS Patuxent River, Maryland, Mr. Craig D. Smith, External Relations, McDonnell Douglas, The Public Affairs Office of the Naval Air Systems Command, COMNAVAIRLANT, NAS Norfolk, Virginia, Ms. Donna Lowe, Public Affairs Office, NAS Lemoore, California, and Mr. Kearny Bothwell, Hughes Aircraft, Radar Systems Division.

Most photographs in this book are credited to their contributors. Photos with no credit indicated were taken by the author.

This book is a product of Detail & Scale, Inc. which has sole responsibility for the contents and layout.

FIRST EDITION
THIRD PRINTING

Published in United States by

TAB BOOKS Inc.
Blue Ridge Summit, PA 17294

Library of Congress Cataloging in Publication Data:

Linn, Don, 1945-
   F-18 Hornet / by Don Linn.
      p. cm. — (Detail & Scale ; vol. 6-)
   Rev. ed. of: F-18 Hornet in detail & scale.
c1982.
      ISBN 0-8306-8016-0 (pbk. : v. 1)
   1. Hornet (Jet fighter plane)
I. Linn, Don, 1945- F-18 Hornet in detail & scale.
II. Title.
UG1242.F5L56   1987   623.74'64—dc19

Published in Great Britain
by Airlife Publishing Ltd.
7 St. John's Hill, Shrewsbury,
SY1 1JE

British Library Cataloging in Publication Data:

Linn, Don
F-18 in Detail and Scale
1 Hornet (Fighter Plane)
1. Title
623.74'63   UG1242.F5
ISBN 0-85368-524-X

Questions regarding the content of this book should be addressed to:

Reader Inquiry Branch
Editorial Department
TAB BOOKS Inc.
Blue Ridge Summit, PA 17294

FRONT COVER: *F-18A, 161214, an early production Hornet assigned to VX-4, during a test flight near NAS Patuxent River.* (McDonnell Douglas)

REAR COVER: *Cockpit in a F/A-18.* (McDonnell Douglas)

The first F/A-18 Hornet prototype preparing for a test flight at NAS Patuxent River, April 1980.

INTRODUCTION

TAB BOOKS Inc., is pleased to present the first book ever published on the F/A-18 Hornet. Although much has been written about the Hornet in articles, we have provided a detailed and accurate account of this new aircraft's development from the YF-17 Cobra to the present production F-18 Hornet.

As the Hornet program progresses beyond development and flight testing, and begins to enter active service in operational squadrons with the U.S. Navy and Marine Corps, and replaces the F-101 Voodoos of the Canadian Forces, we hope to add another volume on this remarkable aircraft.

The most important, and often times the most difficult, aspect of providing detailed coverage of an aircraft which is under development is accuracy. During development things change rapidly, and new aircraft always seem to have an extra blanket of security guarding them, both military and corporate. Taking this into account, as well as the lack of detailed information readily available on the Hornet, author Don Linn has done an outstanding job. He visited NAS Patuxent River to receive up-to-date

briefings from Navy and Marine test pilots and technical representatives on the progress of the Hornet program. McDonnell Douglas provided the various loft drawings and data from which the 1/72nd scale five-view drawings were developed. Technical data was obtained from the F-18 NATOPS manual, and was released by the Naval Air Systems Command after review. It has taken the efforts and cooperation of these organizations, and many other contributors listed on the opposite page, more than two years to compile the information, drawings, and photographs that appear on the following pages. Most of the photographs have never been published before, and many were taken specifically for this publication.

As always, these efforts were undertaken with the aviation enthusiast and scale modeler in mind. On the pages that follow, we believe that Don Linn and the combined design and research talents of the Detail & Scale staff, have done a masterful job in compiling this thorough coverage of the F/A-18 Hornet.

3

DEVELOPMENT PROGRAM

Northrop's YF-17, seen here at NAS Patuxent River during Navy evaluation, 9 September 1978, provided the basic design from which the McDonnell Douglas F-18 Hornet evolved.

"...The versatility of the F/A-18 to effectively perform both fighter and attack missions provides the battle group commander with options never before available. When in a defensive posture, the Hornet will counter either air or surface threat. Offensively, it will provide both fighter escort and a survivable ordnance delivery vehicle with finite accuracy. This force multiplication effect is not available with any other aircraft in the world. A force structure that includes F-14s in Navy fighter squadrons and F/A-18s in both Navy light attack and Marine fighter squadrons has more combat capability and is significantly more cost effective than any other available alternative..."

VADM Wesley L. McDonald, USN
30 June 1981

Admiral McDonald's remarks seem to tell the whole story of the idea behind the Hornet in one paragraph, but in reality the story is a more complex one dating back to 1972. It was during that year that CNO, Chief of Naval Operations, directed a study be conducted to determine the Navy's future needs for fighter aircraft. Fighter Study Four, as it became known, was comprised of Navy and Marine aviators, all highly qualified individuals, who had to foresee ten to fifteen years into the future and use their knowledge and instincts in an effort to develop requirements for the Navy's next generation of fighter aircraft. This team of experts had to take into consideration the deficiencies found in current fighter aircraft, such as the F-4 Phantom and F-14 Tomcat, which were few, and try to estimate the technological advances that should occur during the next ten to fifteen year period.

From this study came the requirements for the Navy Combat Fighter, VFAX, program; a highly maneuverable and agile aircraft with capabilities to handle compatable weapons sytems such as the Sparrow and Sidewinder missiles. So then, on August 28, 1974, the US Navy issued operational requirements under the VFAX program for a new multimission aircraft. A single design was sought with the versatility to replace both the F-4 Phantom in Marine Corps service, and the Navy's A-7 Corsair, both aircraft having been in service 20 and 18 years respectively.

Replacing the F-4 and A-7 with a single aircraft design would mean a large contract, equating to a lot of money, to the company who was successful in presenting a workable design. Understandably the resulting competition involved the major US aircraft manufacturers; LTV, Grumman, McDonnell Aircraft, Northrop, and General Dynamics. At the same time the Navy was looking for a new aircraft to fulfill the VFAX program requirements, the US Air Force was in the midst of their lightweight fighter competition. General Dynamics and Northrop were the main contenders in that competition, each possessing flying prototypes which were the General Dynamics' YF-16 and Northrop's YF-17. These aircraft took part in a fly-off competition, and the winner, or more important, the loser of that competition would have a major impact on the Navy's VFAX program.

The competition for the Navy's VFAX program was limited to these two aircraft. The designs proposed by McDonnell Douglas, LTV, and Grumman never went beyond the 'paper airplane' stage, that is to say they were merely advanced aircraft designs, but with no actual flying prototypes, whereas Northrop and General Dynamics each had prototype aircraft flying in the Air Force's LWFX fly-off competition, and both possessed favorable design features. The F-16 was the winner of that competition, and is a very capable and agile fighter aircraft, but it was not exactly what the Navy was looking for. The Navy instead opted for Northrop's YF-17 design, but not before McDonnell Douglas and Northrop entered into a new agreement.

Although Northrop had a workable design in the YF-17, Northrop lacked experience as a builder of carrier-suitable aircraft. With McDonnell Douglas' long standing as a respected builder of Navy aircraft, coupled with the advanced technology presented in the McDonnell Douglas model 263, a new design with space age electronics and movable canard wings, conditions were desirable for the two companies to pool their resources and technology. The end result was McDonnell Douglas would become prime contractor for the newly designated YF-18 Hornet, while Northrop would be sub-contractor building the aft section of the airplane. But this was only for the McDonnell Douglas F-18 Hornet. Should any sales, foreign or domestic, be generated for the land based version, designated F-18L, Northrop would then become prime contractor for that version.

"We've been accused of buying the failing competitor in the Air Force's light weight fighter competition," responds LtCol. Pete Field, F/A-18 Program Manager and Marine Corps F/A-18 test pilot, during a 1979 interview. "The YF-17 was a very fine airplane, and it came off very well in that competition. We chose the YF-17 because we had to have an airplane with a larger system in it." Continuing, Field adds,

"The F-16 simply doesn't have enough, or is not large enough, to carry the sort of airborne weapons systems we needed. We had to look for a larger version airplane which the YF-16 couldn't be dressed out for." That is the primary reason for the selection of the YF-17 over the YF-16, but there was also strong consideration given to the new General Electric F404 engine which was proving to be a great success in the YF-17.

From Cobra to Hornet

The YF-17, or F-18 Hornet as it became with the agreement reached between McAir and Northrop, was a far different aircraft from its YF-17 progenitor when it first rolled off the production line at McDonnell Douglas.

Outwardly the YF-17 and F-18 bear a strong resemblance to each other, but beyond this they are two completely different aircraft. The changes came about rapidly as McAir set forth to navalize Northrop's Cobra. First, the fuselage and landing gear had to be strengthened to take the load catapult stress creates, as well as that created by arrested landings aboard a carrier. As a direct result, due to the additional weight added in strengthening the fuselage and landing gear, the wing area was increased. Also, more internal fuel capacity was added to meet mission requirements. A carrier arrestor hook was also added.

Next, and again due to mission requirements, new radar systems had to be added to make the new F-18 an all-weather aircraft which the YF-17 was not. And the weapons systems had to be updated to handle the Sparrow missile which the Navy required for fleet defense.

Northrop's CF-18L, designated "Cobra," during Canadian evaluation in December 1979. This aircraft was in fact a YF-17.

(Marshall)

The first Hornet prototype showing its aerodynamic innovations with full span leading flaps at 30°, while the single slot trailing edge flaps and drop ailerons are also down to the 30° take-off configuration.

(McDonnell Douglas)

More changes followed, including increasing the internal fuel capacity from 5,500 lbs in the YF-17 to 10,800 lbs in the F-18, and the overall effect of these changes resulted in the wing span growing from 14.5 feet on the YF-17 to 15.3 feet on the Hornet. This increased the total wing area from 350 square feet to 400 square feet. Accordingly the take off weight rose from 23,000 lbs to 35,000 lbs in the F-18.

General Electric F404 Turbofan

The new F404 engine in the Hornet is an extension of the YJ101 engine development program found in the YF-17. Upgraded to a larger by-pass turbo-fan than the YJ101, the F404 is a very low ratio turbo-fan engine.

Considered one of the brightest aspects of the Hornet program, the F404 has proved to be an almost fault-free engine, and not by accident. The F404 contract involved the most comprehensive full scale development program ever undertaken by the Navy, totaling 80,000 component test hours and more than 13,000 factory test hours completed by 14 development engines over a 57 month period. This resulted in

an engine rated at 16,000 lbs thrust, but weighing only 2,135 lbs, nearly half the weight of the J79 in the F-4 Phantom. The F404 has about the same thrust at half the weight and three-fourths the length! But the most amazing feature of this new engine is that it has 7,700 fewer parts than the J79 in the F-4, containing fewer stages, fewer frames, and fewer bearings.

The first F404 engine went to test in January 1977 and met all performance requirements. The third engine (initial engine shipped to the Naval Air Propulsion Center) began exploratory testing in April 1977, and successfully completed altitude tests in March 1978. The first F404 was shipped to McDonnell Douglas in St. Louis by General Electric in June 1978 for the first flight test which was scheduled for that fall.

Nine F404 flight test engines were delivered in 1978, and 24 F404s were delivered in 1979 to support F/A-18 flight testing.

Speaking with experience, Col. Field describes the F404's quick response, "It is an incredibly fast responding engine that goes from idle to full afterburner in about 3 seconds. It's so fast that it almost comes on sooner than you wanted. We're accus-

F-18/TF-18 Hornet Prototype (FSD) and Production Aircraft Production Block and Serial Numbers.

Prototypes (12 aircraft)

Bureau Numbers	Ship Numbers	Test Function
160775	F 1	Flying Qualities and Flutter
160776	F 2	Propulsion and Performance
160777	F 3	Carrier Suitability, Environmental Control Systems
160778	F 4	Structural Test
160779	F 5	Avionics and Weapons Systems
160780	F 6	High Angle of Attack, Spin Test
160781	TF 1	Armament and Systems
160782	F 7	Armament and Systems
160783	F 8	Performance and Systems
* 160784	TF 2	Accelerated Service Test for F404 Engine
160785	F 9	Maintenance Engineering

* Crashed 8 Sept. 80, Middle Wallop Army Airfield, England.

Pilot Production Batch, FY '79 (9 aircraft)

161213	F 10
161214	F 11
** 161215	F 12
161216	F 13
161217	TF 3
161248	F 14
161249	TF 4
161250	F 15
161251	F 16

** Crashed 14 Nov 80 in Chesapeake Bay, near NAS Patuxent River.

First Production Block, FY80 (25 aircraft)

161353	F 17
161354	TF 5
161355	TF 6
161356	TF 7
161357	TF 8
161358	F 18
161359	F 19
161360	TF 9
161361	F 20
161362	F 21
161363	F 22
161364	F 23
161365	F 24
161366	F 25
161367	F 26
161519	F 27
161520	F 28
161521	F 29
161522	F 30
161523	F 31
161524	F 32
161525	F 33
161526	F 34
161527	F 35
161528	F 36

tomed to a little lag there from experience gained in other airplanes, and we are pleasantly surprised with the acceleration and deceleration response. That gives you better thrust control which is highly desirable in air combat maneuvering." In addition to Col. Field's remarks on the Hornet's quick response is its ability to accelerate from 530 miles per hour, at 35,000 feet, to 1,060 miles per hour in under two minutes.

Other engine-related features aboard the Hornet are the airframe-mounted accessory drive system and the auxiliary power unit. These devices allow the pilot to start his engines without external power. They also permit full ground checkout of all aircraft systems requiring electricity, hydraulic power, fuel pres-

The second Hornet, 160776, arrived shortly after number one in the spring of 1979 to test propulsion and performance of the GE F404 engines.

AIRCRAFT GENERAL ARRANGEMENT

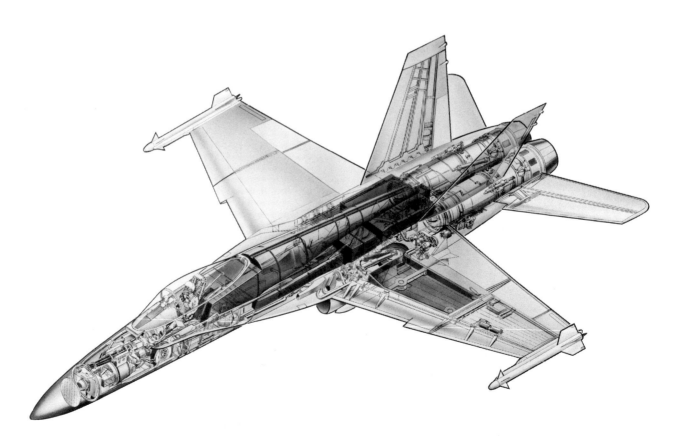

Early production changes are evident on Hornet 5 during a May 1981 flight demonstration at Andrews AFB. Eighty percent of the slots in the leading edge extension (LEX) have been filled in. The "snag" in both the stabilator and wing leading edge have been removed to help reduce drag.

sure or cooling, all without having to start the engines and without external power.

Hughes AN/APG-65 Radar System

In giving the Hornet an all-weather capability, which the YF-17 didn't have, the new Hughes AN/APG-65 radar was added. Rail-mounted for ease of maintenance, and designed specifically for the F/A-18's one man, head-up, Hands-On-Throttle-And-Stick (HOTAS) operation, this new radar system has a programmable signal processor for greater mode flexibility.

The Hughes system offers a full spectrum of air-to-air and air-to-ground capabilities. Air-to-air features Track-While-Scan and three optional air combat maneuvering modes in a system designed for all-altitude, all-aspect coverage. As an attack aircraft the Hornet's radar provides the pilot with a high resolution mapping capability as well as a complete set of modes for the delivery of a variety of ordnance against fixed or moving targets, on both land and sea, in good weather or low visibility conditions.

In addition, the AN/APG-65 with its multimode doppler system, can detect, track, and draw a bead on hostile airborne targets, day or night, and in any weather. It also incorporates high and medium pulse repetition frequencies (PRFs) to provide all-aspect

search and track capability that can be used at any operational altitude. Low PRFs are used for certain functions in air-to-air as well as air-to-ground missions.

In the air superiority role, using track-while-scan (TWS), Hornet pilots are able to track multiple targets, displaying up to eight targets on the MFD screen, while maintaining up to ten targets in a track file in the computer. At the same time, a raid assessment mode allows the pilot to choose between closely spaced targets that may be attacking.

The head-up Hands-On-Throttle-And-Stick (HOTAS) concept is an important feature for single pilot system operation. With this feature the radar controls are mounted on the stick and throttle allowing the pilot the capability of selecting and firing any of the air-to-air weapons, and at the same time, control the radar during air combat maneuvering while maintaining visual contact with the target.

In air-to-surface attack or interdiction missions, the Hughes system features long range surface mapping. With this capability is a dual-plane terrain avoidance mode to assist in penetration at night or under limited visibility. Also, air-to-ground ranging is provided by the radar when a target is designated from the forward-looking infrared (FLIR) sensor, head-up display (HUD), laser spot tracker (LST), or on the

The Hughes AN/APG-65 radar provides the Hornet pilot with three acquisition modes, as well as a raid assessment mode that allows the pilot to choose between closely spaced targets. **(Hughes)**

multi-function display (MFD). It is also the first time radar, FLIR, and laser spot tracking have been employed in a single system. In delivery of air-to-ground ordnance, the radar information and weapons release data is displayed on both the HUD and multi-purpose display.

For air combat maneuvering, when targets are in ranges from 500 feet to five nautical miles, the Hornet radar has three acquisition modes. When the pilot selects the vertical acquisition mode, the radar searches a 5.3° width directly ahead of the F-18, and through a 74° arc in the vertical plane of the aircraft at the rate of two seconds per frame. The HUD acquisition mode scans a 20° by 20° square area, as seen through the HUD at the same rate, automatically locking onto the first target detected. The pilot may reject that target and the radar will automatically progress to the next target. A boresight mode, the third acquisition mode, is also available, allowing the Hornet pilot to spotlight a target on the boresight axis.

First Flight

After nearly three and a half years of development

work on the first F/A-18 prototype, Hornet number 1 (BuNo. 160775) was ready for its first flight. Jack Krings, McDonnell Douglas chief test pilot, taxied the F/A-18 from the McDonnell Douglas ramp onto the runway of the Lambert-St. Louis International Airport on the morning of November 18, 1978 to prepare for the Hornet's first take-off. Following all the preflight checks and engine runup, Krings pushed the Hornet's throttles to take-off power. Effortlessly the General Electric F404 engines accelerated as the F/A-18 began its take-off roll down the runway, rotating, and in the air for the first time at 11:05 a.m. CST. A McDonnell Douglas F-4 Phantom and F-15 Eagle followed to accompany the Hornet on its maiden flight from St. Louis to Springfield, Illinois and back again, landing at 11:55 a.m. During the fifty minute flight, Krings climbed up to 24,000 feet and reached a top speed of 300 knots.

Patuxent River

Initial flight tests continued at St. Louis until January 1979 when the Hornet moved to NAS Patuxent River, Maryland to participate in a new prototype

COCKPIT LAYOUT

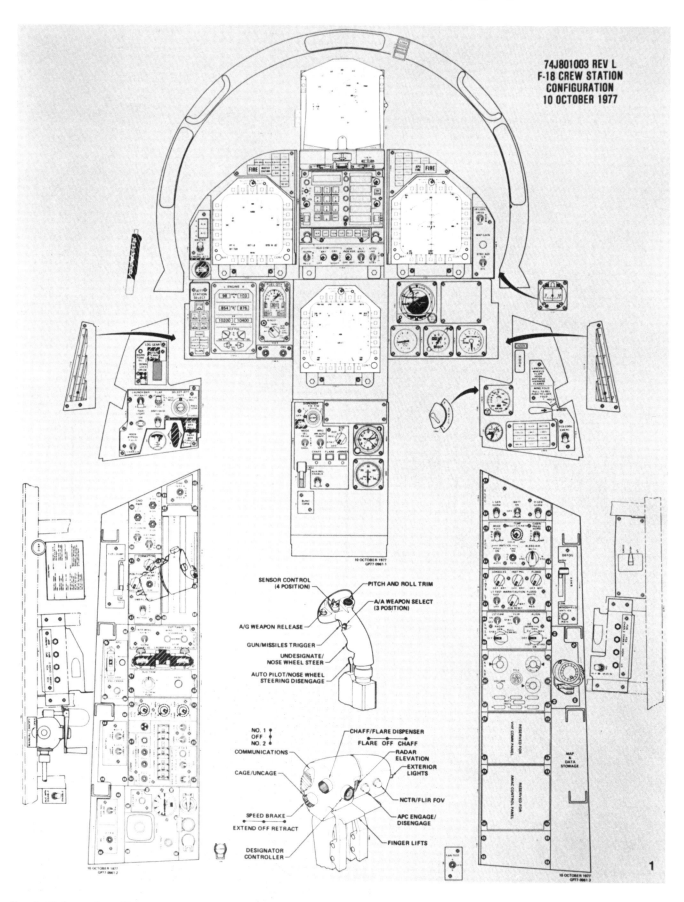

74J801003 REV L
F-18 CREW STATION
CONFIGURATION
10 OCTOBER 1977

SENSOR CONTROL
(4 POSITION)

PITCH AND ROLL TRIM

A/A WEAPON SELECT
(3 POSITION)

A/G WEAPON RELEASE

GUN/MISSILES TRIGGER

UNDESIGNATE/
NOSE WHEEL STEER

AUTO PILOT/NOSE WHEEL
STEERING DISENGAGE

NO. 1
OFF
NO. 2

CHAFF/FLARE DISPENSER

FLARE OFF CHAFF

COMMUNICATIONS

RADAR
ELEVATION

CAGE/UNCAGE

EXTERIOR
LIGHTS

NCTR/FLIR FOV

SPEED BRAKE

APC ENGAGE/
DISENGAGE

EXTEND OFF RETRACT

FINGER LIFTS

DESIGNATOR
CONTROLLER

Cockpit layout as it appeared in early Hornets.

(U.S. Navy)

Hornet 6 awaiting its next test flight on the ramp at Patuxent River.   *(Brown)*

Hornet 7 with 500 pound bombs on the inboard pylons, and cameras to photograph their release and separation on the outboard pylons.

(Brown)

testing program called 'Principal Site Concept'. With the Principal Site Concept, all testing is done at one test site, Patuxent River in this case, reducing the need to have a greater number of test aircraft spread over several different test sites performing different test functions. Beside being practical from a logistics standpoint, it also provides for a better working relationship between the Navy and McDonnell Douglas personnel, giving each the opportunity to work closely together exchanging ideas and discussing problems face to face.

Hornet 160775 was the first of twelve F/A-18 prototypes built by McDonnell Douglas that formed the Full Scale Development (FSD) program at Patuxent River. The FSD program ended in the summer of 1982, when, at that time, the US Navy took over the remaining testing. The twelve FSD Hornets continued flight tests, and by May of 1980 the F-18s had logged more than 1,000 hours of flight tests in 800 flights. The second and third Hornets, 160776 and 160777 respectively, had arrived with number 3 taking part in environmental tests at the Naval Air Engineering Center, Lakehurst, New Jersey.

Hornet number 4, by this time, had also arrived at Patuxent River to participate in the FSD program. During one test flight in early spring 1980, number 4 reached a negative load factor of 2.8. It also performed additional flying qualities and crosswind landing work as part of its test function.

Back in St. Louis, the second two seat Hornet, TF 2, and the ninth single seat Hornet, F 9, both painted in the production gray camouflage scheme for the first time, were taking part in a demonstration of aircraft reliability and accelerated service testing of the F404 engines known as the 'Hornet Hustle'. In 55 available flight days, the two Hornets accumulated nearly 150 flight hours in 116 flights. This included six flights per day on three separate occasions by F 9.

By November 1980, two years after the first flight, F/A-18 Hornets at Patuxent River were averaging more than 50 flights per week, giving the Hornet more than 2,500 flight hours with ten FSD Hornets and four

Hornet 6, painted in orange trim for increased visibility of the aircraft during spin testing. (McDonnell Douglas)

AILERON/TRAILING EDGE FLAP AND FULL SPAN LEADING EDGE FLAP CONFIGURATION

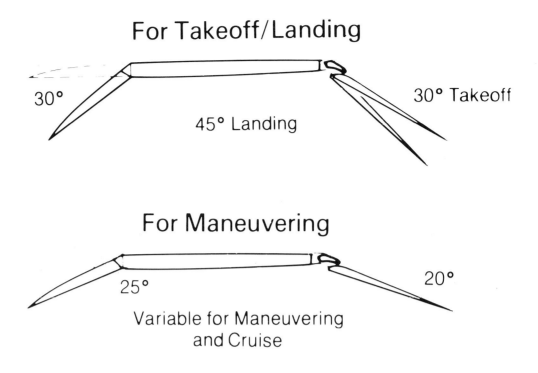

For Takeoff/Landing

30°

45° Landing

30° Takeoff

For Maneuvering

25°

20°

Variable for Maneuvering
and Cruise

The Hornet's straight wings with large, powerful flaps allows a flat, slow carrier approach. In the approach configuration the ailerons droop 45° with the flaps. The leading and trailing edge flaps are computer programmed to deflect for optimum lift and drag while in either maneuvering or cruise conditions.

(McDonnell Douglas)

pilot production Hornets now taking part in the test program. Also during this period, in the midst of ongoing development testing, the fourth of five Navy Preliminary Evaluations (NPE) and the Initial Operational Test and Evaluation (IOT&E) was being conducted at Patuxent River.

This latter IOT&E phase was the Navy's first opportunity to evaluate the Hornet in a squadron setting, or atmosphere. The Navy's VX-4 test squadron flew and maintained three of the pilot production Hornets, carrying the squadrons XF tailcode, with McAir technical support. VX-4, near the end of 1980, continued follow-on testing and evaluation at the Pacific Missile Test Center at Point Mugu, California.

The Navy Preliminary Evaluation, conducted by Marine Corps and Navy test pilots, flew more than seventy flights gaining 125 flight hours. They flew nearly twice the speed of sound, endured loads greater than 7 gs., and exceeded 90° angle of attack. The test pilots also flew sorties for bomb separation, airborne gunfire, radar intercepts, and performance qualities.

The FSD program continued at Patuxent River through 1981, constantly adding up the number of flight hours, not only for the aircraft, but also for the pilots who have to fly it, which is equally important.

Changes were incorporated into the airframe as test results dictated, while Hornet pilots gained additional knowledge of the Hornet's capabilities.

During the year flutter evaluation flights were conducted with the new configuration cylindrical external fuel tanks. The new design 330 gallon tanks offer a 15 gallon greater fuel capacity over the original 315 gallon eliptical tanks.

During the weapons testing program at Patuxent River, air-to-ground separations included Mk.82 bombs, LAU-61 rocket launcher pods and BDU-12 practice bombs. Bomb and gun accuracy evaluation flights continued, demonstrating good results.

Accelerated service tests on Hornet F 14 resumed after the re-installation of the F404 engines previously sent to General Electric facilities in Lynn, Mass., for teardown, inspection, and reassembly. By October 1981 total accelerated service time reached nearly 300 flight hours.

Also in October the last FSD Hornet, F 9, returned to St. Louis for tie down, its portion of the program, electro-mechanical compatibility and maintenance engineering, was completed.

Another October 1981 event worth noting was the Hornet's attack range demonstration. On October 13, Hornet F 14 took-off from NAS Patuxent River armed with four 1,000 pound Mk.83 bombs, three external fuel tanks, two AIM-9 Sidewinder missiles, a forward-looking infrared (FLIR) pod, and a laser spot tracker and strike camera (LST/SCAM) pod, to complete an attack mission 620 miles from base. The target for this mission was the Pinecastle complex near Orlando, Fla. Operating unrefueled, and making a successful delivery of its ordnance, Hornet F 14 returned to Patuxent River with sufficient fuel remaining in its three external fuel tanks to loiter for ten minutes, simulating the delay an aircraft might experience in the carrier landing pattern.

Landing with 1,600 pounds of fuel remaining, the pilot executed a touch-and-go landing, again to simulate a carrier approach, re-entered the pattern and landed. More than 1,200 pounds of fuel were still aboard at engine shut-down. In announcing the results of this test strike mission, U.S. Navy officials noted that, "total time for the mission was slightly more than three hours. The mission was flown with a Full-Scale Development aircraft, which has 700 pounds less fuel than do production models."

By the end of 1981, Hornets completed more than 6,000 flight hours flown in over 4,000 sorties for development, training, and testing in twenty-two aircraft.

Continuing the FSD program at Patuxent River into 1982, the F/A-18 made its first fully automatic hands-off landing at the Naval Air Test Center. Believed to be the first time in Naval history that an aircraft flew to touchdown on its initial automatic landing system test flight, the January 22 event was a great success.

The test was performed to demonstrate Hornet's suitability for carrier operations, including the F-18's compatibility with the Fleet's Automatic Carrier Landing System (ACLS). The ACLS and approach power compensator (APC) aboard the Hornet are in full command of the aircraft's flight controls and throttles during approach and landing.

At a pre-designated point several miles from the landing threshold, the Hornet pilot couples his radar to the ACLS SPN-42 radar aboard the carrier. The radar transmits a signal to guide the aircraft onto the carrier deck. Signals fed to the Hornet's autopilot system are translated into movements of the stick and control surfaces.

The ACLS compensates for the motion of the carrier deck, timing the Hornet's approach and touch-down to the rolling and pitching deck. Power changes are made by the APC to keep the aircraft at the proper speed for landing.

"Control was excellent, and the approach was right on the mark," said McDonnell Douglas test pilot Pete Pilcher, the pilot of the test flight. "This should make an excellent system for hands-off recovery aboard ship in the dark or bad weather."

Following Pilcher, Navy pilots completed their first Hornet hands-off landing four days later as part of the Navy's concurrent evaluation of the F/A-18's automatic landing system.

As Hornet testing continues for the remainder of 1982, the first Hornet training squadron, VFA-125 at NAS Lemoore, is busy turning out the first Hornet

With wings folded, an F-18 taxies into position for a simulated catapult launch at NAS Patuxent River.
(McDonnell Douglas)

Hornet 7 launches an AIM-9L from an underwing pylon. Note the AIM-7 Sparrow under the other wing.
(McDonnell Douglas)

Number 7 with two high drag bombs under the fuselage. Note the cameras mounted on the wing tips to photograph the weapons' separation from the aircraft.
(McDonnell Douglas)

Hornet 4 tanking from the U.S. Navy's only Convair 880 during a January 1982 test flight.

instructor pilots who began their work in July. It is at that time that the first Hornet squadron will be commissioned. VMFA-314, a Marine Corps F-4 squadron, is the first squadron to begin transition to the F/A-18 during July, 1982. Following close behind will be two additional Marine Corps F-4 squadrons, VMFA-323 and VMFA-531, both scheduled to begin transition during the late summer of 1982. The Navy's first Hornet squadrons, VA-146 and VA-147, both A-7 squadrons from NAS Lemoore, will begin their transition in 1983-84.

The wheels of Hornet 7 are just about to make contact with the runway at Patuxent River following a 1980 test flight.

The refueling probe on the Hornet is very similar to the refueling probe on the F-4 Phantom, as can be seen on Hornet 6 refueling from a KA-3 tanker. *(McDonnell Douglas)*

McAir technicians servicing Hornet 8 during the Full Scale Development Program at Patuxent River.

By April 1980, Hornet 5 had already scored three radio controlled drone kills which the line crew promptly recorded just below the windscreen.

Right: By fall 1981, the number of drone kills on F 5 rose to twelve. Eight were scored with Sidewinder missiles, and four with Sparrow missiles.

Below: McDonnell Douglas technicians preparing Hornet 7 for a test flight in April 1980. The muzzle of the Hornet's 20 mm cannon is visible between the anti-glare panel and the radome. Just below the windscreen is a single kill mark of a radio controlled drone with a Sidewinder intersecting it.

SEA TRIALS

Hornet 3 approaching the flight deck of the USS America during sea trials. Pilots report the Hornet caught the number 3 wire in 75 percent of the 32 arrested landings aboard America. *(McDonnell Douglas)*

An important part of the F/A-18 evaluation, just as important as its fighter/attack capabilities, is its compatibility within the aircraft carrier environment and its reliability at sea. Sea trials would indicate the success, or failure, of both.

Hornet's five days of sea trials, 30 October through 3 November 1979, began when F/A-18 test pilot LCdr Dick Richards landed Hornet F 3 aboard the USS America just before sunset on October 30. Departing Patuxent River with a TA-7 piloted by Lt. Ken Grubb as chase plane, Richards made the one hour flight to the USS America which was steaming 65 miles off the Virginia coast, made a series of low approaches and touch-and-go landings before landing on America's deck, catching the number 3 wire with no problem.

The two Navy pilots, Richards and Grubb, alternating at the controls, made thirty-two launches and arrested landings during the six flying periods from 30 October through 3 November. Considered by some to be the most successful initial sea trials in modern history, long hours of preparation led the way. McAir test pilots, in preparing the Hornet for sea trials, performed ninety-two field catapults and arrested landings at Patuxent River. Richards and Grubb each had twenty-five hours of flight time in the Hornet, including twenty field catapults and arrested landings, also at Patuxent River.

Approaching the carrier, the F/A-18 proved to be very stable on the glide slope. It approached at a nominal 4° pitch attitude which provided an excellent field of vision of the carrier. Seventy-five percent of the 32 arrested landings caught the number 3 wire, and there were no unintentional bolters. Two intentional bolters were made to check hook point wear. The Hornet exhibited excellent characteristics during cable engagement with very little aircraft rolling action during cable run-out.

"The two Navy pilots that have participated in this project, myself and Lt. Ken Grubb," said LCdr Richards, "have been very pleased with what we've seen so far to date. The airplane is very stable on the glide slope, and we found ourselves able to make very small glide slope corrections that are required for carrier landings."

Catapult launches proved as equally successful as the arrested landings. Hook-ups were made easy by using the HUD's (Head-Up Display) aircraft centerline mark. The pilot places this mark on the catapult track and line-up is almost automatic. All launches were made 'hands off'. During the sea trials minimum excess speed and cross-wind catapult shots were performed. While most launches were done with intermediate power, two of the 32 launches were made at max afterburner. The Hornet was launched from both the bow and waist cats during the

Catching the number 3 wire, the Hornet completed successful sea trials on 3 November 1979.

(McDonnell Douglas)

five days aboard America.

"The catapult launch characteristics are excellent," said LCdr Richards, "allowing us to have hands-off catapult shot capability that we consider a very desirable and a very safe feature in naval aviation."

Along with launch and recovery compatibility, sea trials were needed to determine the Hornet's deck handling characteristics as well as aircraft reliability and availability.

Deck crew handling was demonstrated through a series of tests such as aircraft tie down at various spots on the flight deck and hanger deck, and operations on the elevator with other aircraft.

Throughout the sea trials the F/A-18 demonstrated 100% aircraft availability, allowing the testing to be carried out uninterrupted. The F404 engines were started at one time with a 22 knot wind blowing up its tailpipe to demonstrate its reliability. Engine starting using the onboard APU was routine.

Number 3 on the elevator during sea trials.

(McDonnell Douglas)

TF-18 HORNET

The first two-seat Hornet, T 1, Climbing after take-off *from Patuxent River.*

The first TF-18 Hornet arrived at NAS Patuxent River on 19 December 1979, several weeks following its first flight and subsequent flight testing at St. Louis. Joining the six single seat F-18 Hornets then at Patuxent River, this was the first of two TF-18s to take part in the full scale development flight test program.

A two-seat version of the Hornet was under consideration from the beginning. It has the same overall dimensions as the single-seat Hornet. Installing the second seat and a full second cockpit required reducing the internal fuel capacity in the Hornet by about 6 percent. It is also designed to be fully combat capable, allowing the TF-18 to be switched from training duties to combat strike or fighter missions with the same efficiency as the single seat F/A-18.

Current plans call for 150 TF-18 Hornets to be built out of the 1,377 Hornets on order, or roughly a ratio of 9:1. The TF-18 Hornet will play a major role in the Hornet training program. In fact the majority of Hornets now assigned to VFA-125 are TF-18s, allowing for efficient student-instructor pilot training.

The excellent all-around visibility of the Hornet's canopy is evident on the second TF-18 prototype.
(McDonnell Douglas)

Hornet T1 waiting for clearance prior to take-off from Patuxent River.

The second two-seat Hornet performed accelerated service tests of the General Electric F404 engine.
(McDonnell Douglas)

Early production TF-18 assigned to VFA-125 during extended deployment to MCAS Yuma in January 1982.
(Huston)

FOREIGN SALES

The first of 138 CF-18 Hornets for Canada undergoes final assembly at McDonnell Douglas facilities in St. Louis. *(McDonnell Douglas)*

Foreign sales, an important consideration in any new aircraft development program, has become an important element in the ongoing Hornet program.

Several interested countries have sent government and military leaders to St. Louis to examine and see first hand the Hornet's capabilities. Through these inspections, and the Hornet's demonstrated performance to date, foreign sales for the Hornet look very promising. Spain, Greece, Turkey, Canada, Australia and Israel have all looked at the Hornet with keen interest, but only Canada, and recently Australia, have bought the F/A-18.

Canada became the first country to purchase the F/A-18. In an announcement on April 10, 1980, by Canadian Defense Minister Gilles Lemontagne, Canada became what is hoped to be the first of many potential foreign countries to purchase the Hornet. The signing ceremonies in Ottawa culminated many years of effort by McDonnell Douglas and the Canadian government. The decision, worth an estimated $2.37 billion, calls for delivery of the first of 130 Hornets, designated CF-18, in late 1982. Deliveries of the remaining CF-18s will continue through late 1989.

An interesting sidelight to Canada becoming the first foreign purchaser of the Hornet, in a very remote way like history repeating itself, is the fact that Canada was the first foreign country to purchase a McDonnell aircraft. It was in 1955, when a then struggling aircraft manufacturer received its first foreign contract, when the Royal Canadian Navy bought the McDonnell F2H-3 Banshee, which like the Hornet, was a naval fighter. It seems fitting that the Hornet is maintaining the relationship that began 27 years ago.

Australia became the second country to purchase the Hornet when Minister of Defense Denis J. Killen made the announcement on October 20, 1981.

Seventy-five Hornets are on order for the Royal Australian Air Force at an overall cost of $2.39 billion. The cost includes some configuration changes to meet RAAF operational requirements, plus the cost of simulators, spares, test equipment, training equipment, and overhaul facilities at RAAF bases.

The first RAAF Hornets are expected near the end of 1984, with operational training beginning by mid 1985.

The Australian Hornets will be assembled and tested at the government aircraft factories at Avalon. Engines will be assembled at the Commonwealth Aircraft Corporation at Melbourne.

The Hornet was chosen after a long evaluation by the Australian defense ministry in which the two finalists were the F-18 and the General Dynamics F-16. "We had to choose between two magnificent aircraft," said Killen, "however, it has become clear that, in relation to operational factors, the F-18 will be better suited to our needs."

No other immediate prospects for foreign sales are evident, although Spain and several other NATO air forces are watching closely as the Hornet begins to enter fleet service with the Navy and Marines.

F-18 WEAPONRY

LASER SPOT TRACKER (LST) POD (FUSELAGE MOUNTED)

315 GALLON EXTERNAL FUEL TANK

FWD LOOKING INFRARED (FLIR) POD (FUSELAGE MOUNTED)

MK84 LASER GUIDED BOMB (LGB)

AIM-9L SIDEWINDER GUIDED MISSILE (AIR-TO-AIR)

MK82 LASER GUIDED BOMB (LGB)

WALLEYE I (ER/DL) GUIDED WEAPON (AIR-TO-GROUND)

B57 BOMB

AGM-88A HARM GUIDED MISSILE (AIR-TO-GROUND)

MK82 INFRARED GUIDED BOMB (IRGB)

AIM-7F SPARROW GUIDED MISSILE (AIR-TO-AIR)

AN/AWW-7B (MODIFIED) DATA LINK POD (WALLEYE)

M61A1 20mm GUN

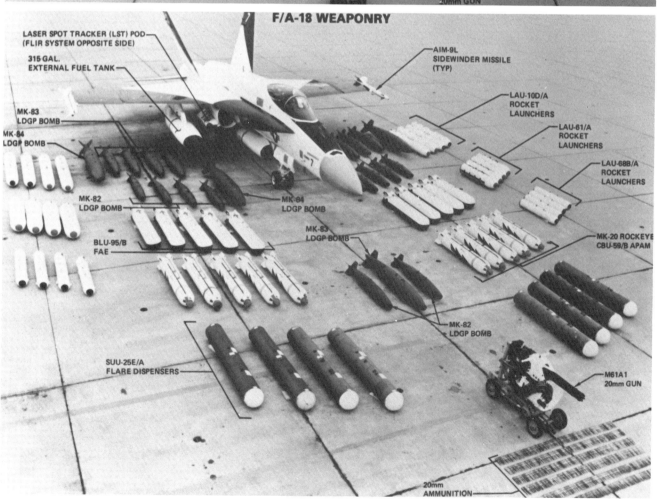

F/A-18 WEAPONRY

LASER SPOT TRACKER (LST) POD (FLIR SYSTEM OPPOSITE SIDE)

315 GAL. EXTERNAL FUEL TANK

MK-83 LDGP BOMB

MK-84 LDGP BOMB

MK-82 LDGP BOMB

BLU-95/B FAE

MK-84 LDGP BOMB

MK-83 LDGP BOMB

AIM-9L SIDEWINDER MISSILE (TYP)

LAU-10D/A ROCKET LAUNCHERS

LAU-61/A ROCKET LAUNCHERS

LAU-68B/A ROCKET LAUNCHERS

MK-20 ROCKEYE CBU-59/B APAM

SUU-25E/A FLARE DISPENSERS

MK-82 LDGP BOMB

M61A1 20mm GUN

20mm AMMUNITION

AIR-TO-AIR MISSILES

AIM-9L Sidewinder missile mounted on a TF-18 wing tip. *(Huston)*

Hornet 5 launching a Sparrow missile. *(McDonnell Douglas)*

This AIM-7 Sparrow appears as a blur as it is launched from Hornet 7. *(McDonnell Douglas)*

AIR-TO-GROUND WEAPONS

During long range attack missions, Hornets can carry an impressive war load. This Hornet flew 1,240 miles non-stop without in-flight refueling, dropped four 1,000 pound bombs on target, returned to base and made practice approaches. Along with the four 1,000 pound bombs, the Hornet also carried three 315 gallon drop tanks, a Laser Spot Tracker on the right Sparrow station, a FLIR pod on the left Sparrow station, and two AIM-9L Sidewinders on the wing tips.
(McDonnell Douglas)

High drag bombs on the centerline and outboard wing pylons flank a fuel tank on the inboard wing pylon on Hornet 3.
(McDonnell Douglas)

Number 4 releasing 1,000 pound bombs during the FSD flight test program. (McDonnell Douglas)

Hornet 14 loaded with Mk.82 500 pound bombs on multiple ejector racks.

FLIR pod mounted on the left Sparrow station on Hornet 7. (McDonnell Douglas/Yarbrough)

Two 1,000 pound bombs loaded on a horizontal ejector rack. (McDonnell Douglas/Yarbrough)

LANDING GEAR DETAIL

This head-on view shows to good effect the Hornet's stance on its landing gear.

Close-up of the nose landing gear. Note the catapult launch arm and the approach lights.

Left main landing gear detail. Also note the detail of the Sparrow missile and its mount.

NOSE DETAILS

Right side of nose showing open avionics bays, nose landing gear, and intake detail.

Underside of left nose showing pitot tubes, cooling grids, blade antennas, and light. (McDonnell Douglas)

WING FOLD DETAIL

Wing fold detail from above with the wing in the extended position. **(Huston)**

Wing fold joint on the left wing with the wing in the folded position. **(Huston)**

FLAP AND AILERON DETAIL

Trailing edge flap and full-span aileron in the lowered position. **(Huston)**

BOARDING LADDER DETAIL

Extended boarding ladder showing the actuating cylinder. This ladder is unique in design when compared to other ingress/egress ladders on aircraft.

Boarding ladder in the extended position showing the well in the LEX into which the ladder retracts. Note the braces between the ladder and the fuselage.

TAIL DETAILS

Vertical stabilizer and rudder detail showing lights and tape light panels.

Exhaust nozzles and arresting hook detail.

F/A-18 COLORS

The first of eleven McDonnell Douglas F-18 Hornet prototypes on the ramp at NAS Patuxent River, September 1980. This aircraft made its first flight on November 18, 1978.

Two in-flight views of the same aircraft as above. Note the original leading edges on the wings and stabilators.
(McDonnell Douglas)

Hornet prototype number 2, 160776, the propulsion and performance test aircraft, getting a "check-over" by McAir technicians at NAS Patuxent River, May 1979.

COCKPIT COLORS

Front cockpit of an F-18/TF-18 Hornet with HUD located at top center. The display screen on the left is the Master Monitor Display (MMD) for aircraft status. The display screen on the right is the Multi-Function Display (MFD) sensor display, and the screen in the center is the Electronic Horizontal Display, moving map, and navigation display.

The rear instrument panel is basically the same as the front instrument panel, but without the Electronic Warfare Control Systems that appear under the Electronic Horizontal Display.

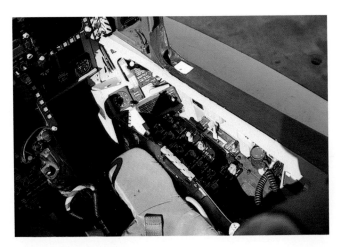

Left console, front cockpit, showing throttles.

Right console, front cockpit.

(All photos on this page are courtesy of Phillip Huston)

Headrest on the F-18's Martin-Baker Mk. 10 Ejection Seat.

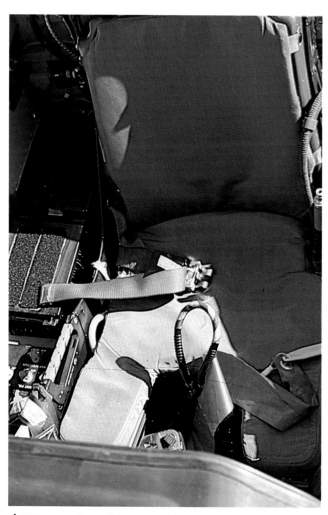

Lower seat cushions and D ring ejection handle.

Lower instrument panel and control stick.

Left console and throttles in the rear cockpit of a TF-18.

(All photos on this page are courtesy of Phillip Huston)

PROTOTYPES 3 & 4

F-18 Hornet prototype number 3 over the USS America during carrier qualifications which were conducted October 31 through November 3, 1980. *(McDonnell Douglas)*

The number 4 prototype refueling from the Navy's only Convair UC-880. Received from the FAA, and modified by Flight Systems International, this aircraft has a KA-3 tanker package for refueling F-18s.

PROTOTYPES 5, 6, & 7

Hornet prototype number 5 on the ramp at NAS Patuxent River with a McAir technician in the cockpit preparing the aircraft for the next sortie.

The spin test Hornet, with bright orange trim, has a parachute in the box located on top of and between the exhaust nozzles to assist in spin recovery.

With movie cameras mounted on the Sidewinder missile rails to photograph the Sparrow missile launches, Hornet prototype number 7 is used to test armament and avionics.

PRODUCTION HORNETS

Appearing in the production camouflage is Hornet number 14, 161248, part of the first production batch. It is carrying 28 MK. 82 bombs.

VX-4 maintained a detachment of F-18s at NAS Patuxent River during 1981 as part of the Navy evaluation. Their test function was later transferred to NAS Point Mugu, California. (Roop)

The first Hornet squadron, VFA-125, was commissioned at NAS Lemoore in November 1980. Comprising both Navy and Marine pilots, VFA-125 is tasked with training Hornet instructor pilots. (McDonnell Douglas)

TF-18 COLORS

Two views of the first TF-18 in flight.   *(McDonnell Douglas)*

TF-18A, 161354, the fifth two-seat Hornet produced, preparing for a training sortie. Assigned to VFA-125, TF-18s are being used to train Hornet instructor pilots.

(Huston)

TF-18 of VFA-125 at NAS Lemoore before application of tail codes or nose number. (Chee)

A TF-18 from VF-125 at NAS Norfolk after a cross-country flight, April 25, 1982.

The large canopy section of the TF-18 provides excellent all-around visibility. Designed with full combat capability in the rear cockpit, the TF-18 is the same in overall dimensions as the single seat F-18.(Huston)

A Navy Hornet takes off with a load of Sparrows, Sidewinders, and bombs. (McDonnell Douglas)

The setting sun makes for an interesting back-lighted photograph of Hornet 3 on the flight deck of the USS America.
(McDonnell Douglas)

A head-on shot of an F/A-18. Note the gun muzzle opening between the radome and the anti-glare panel.
(McDonnell Douglas)

Hornet 4 is shown here with two 500 pound bombs on each of the outboard pylons, and fuel tanks on the inboard pylons.
(Brown)

DIMENSIONS & DATA

Dimension	Actual	1/72nd	1/48th	1/32nd
Wingspan (with missles)	40.4'	6.73"	10.10"	15.15"
Wingspan (without missiles)	37.5'	6.25"	09.38"	14.06"
Wings Folded	27.5'	4.58"	06.88"	10.31"
Length	56.0'	9.33"	14.00"	21.00"
Height	15.3'	2.55"	03.83"	05.74"
Stabilator Span	21.6'	3.60"	05.40"	08.10"
Wheel Tread	10.2'	1.70"	02.55"	03.83"
Wheel Track	17.8'	2.97"	04.45"	06.68"

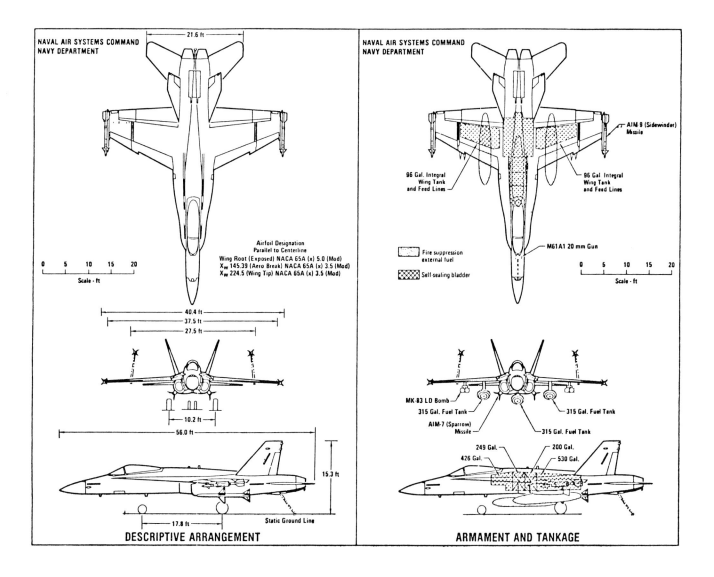

DESCRIPTIVE ARRANGEMENT

ARMAMENT AND TANKAGE

Courtesy of the U.S. Navy.

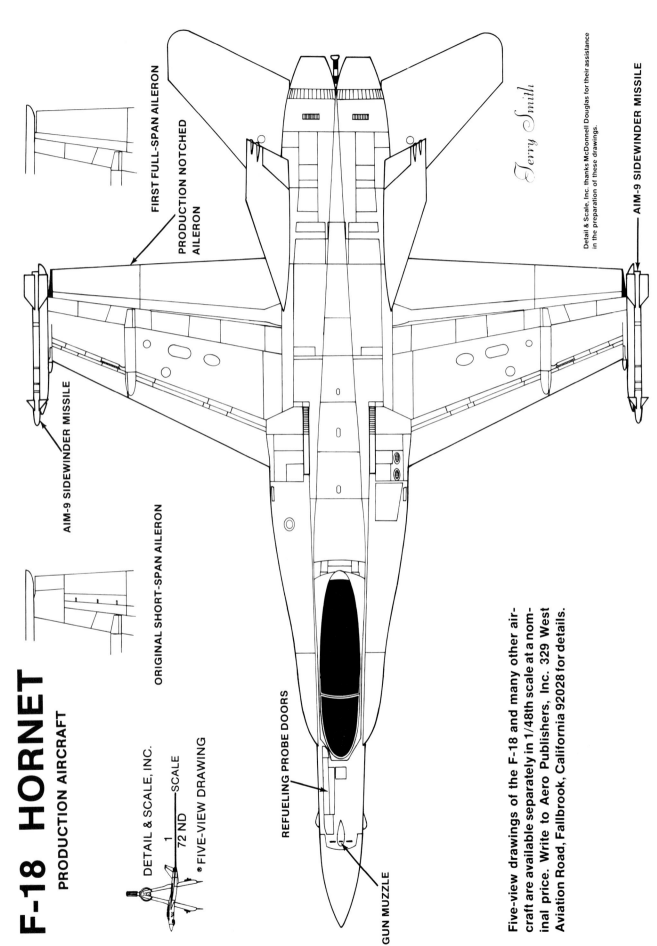

F-18 HORNET
PRODUCTION AIRCRAFT

FIRST FULL-SPAN AILERON

PRODUCTION NOTCHED AILERON

AIM-9 SIDEWINDER MISSILE

ORIGINAL SHORT-SPAN AILERON

AIM-9 SIDEWINDER MISSILE

Terry Smith

REFUELING PROBE DOORS

GUN MUZZLE

DETAIL & SCALE, INC.

1
72 ND ─ SCALE

® FIVE-VIEW DRAWING

Detail & Scale, Inc. thanks McDonnell Douglas for their assistance in the preparation of these drawings.

Five-view drawings of the F-18 and many other aircraft are available separately in 1/48th scale at a nominal price. Write to Aero Publishers, Inc. 329 West Aviation Road, Fallbrook, California 92028 for details.

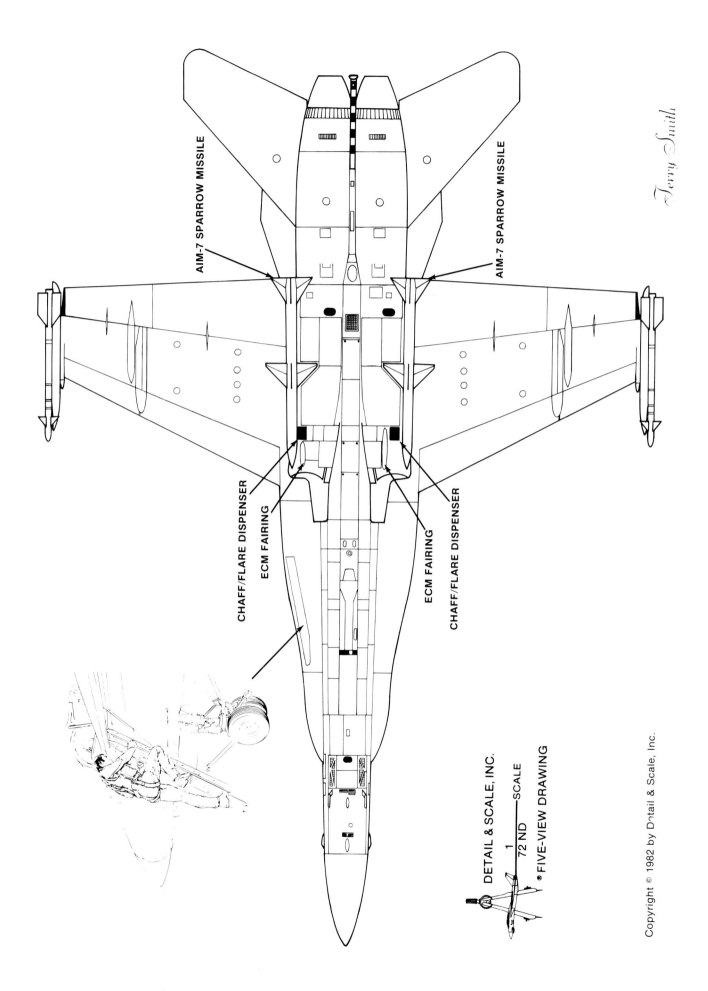

AIM-7 SPARROW MISSILE

AIM-7 SPARROW MISSILE

CHAFF/FLARE DISPENSER

ECM FAIRING

ECM FAIRING

CHAFF/FLARE DISPENSER

Jerry Smith

DETAIL & SCALE, INC.

1
72 ND
SCALE

● FIVE-VIEW DRAWING

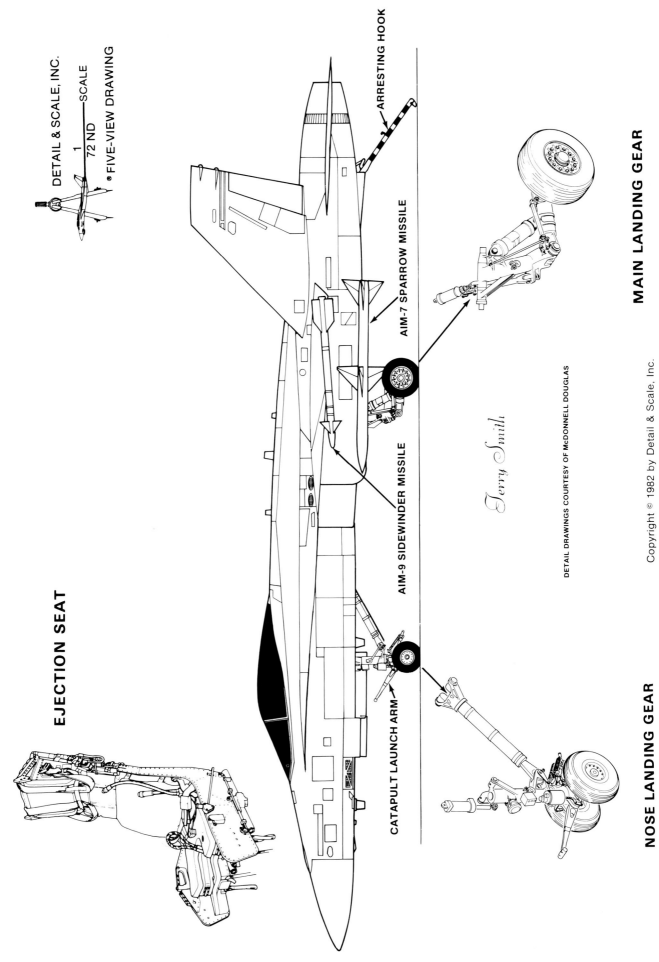

EJECTION SEAT

MAIN LANDING GEAR

NOSE LANDING GEAR

ARRESTING HOOK

AIM-7 SPARROW MISSILE

AIM-9 SIDEWINDER MISSILE

CATAPULT LAUNCH ARM

DETAIL & SCALE, INC.

SCALE

1
72 ND

® FIVE-VIEW DRAWING

Jerry Smith

DETAIL DRAWINGS COURTESY OF McDONNELL DOUGLAS

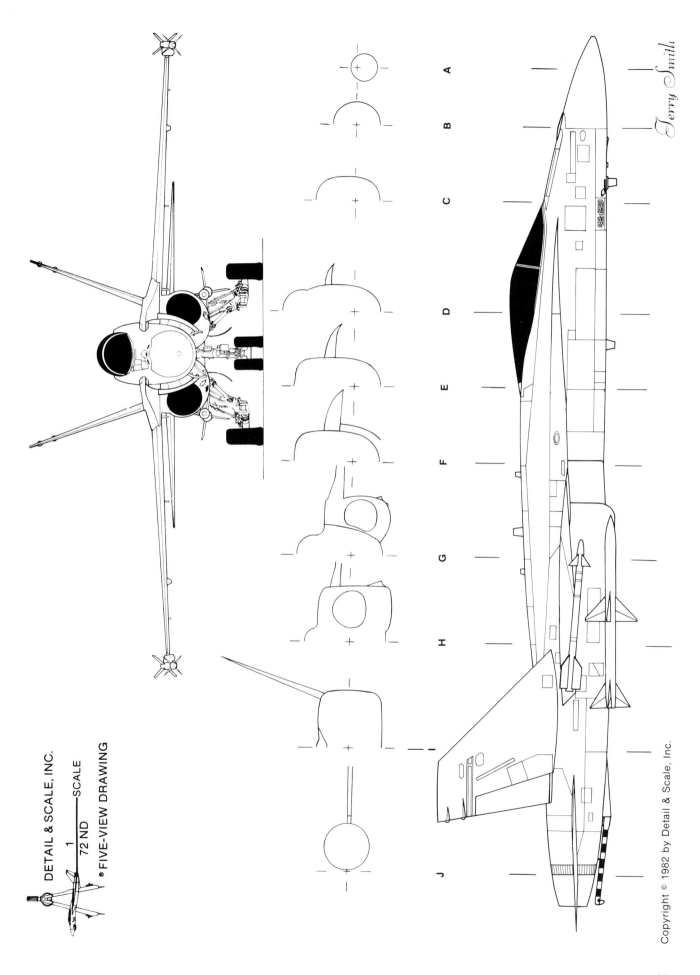

DETAIL & SCALE, INC.

1 —— SCALE
72 ND

®FIVE-VIEW DRAWING

Jerry Smith

Copyright © 1982 by Detail & Scale, Inc.

A B C D E F G H I J

HORNET UPDATES

An early production Hornet with external modifications visible. Eighty percent of the leading edge extension slots are filled in to help reduce drag during high angle of attack. Also note the elimination of the snag in the leading edges of the wing and stabilators. *(McDonnell Douglas)*

The Hornet's Full Scale Development program at Patuxent River was established to determine the F-18's suitability as a Naval fighter/attack aircraft, and to find and correct any deficiencies that may appear in either design or performance during this period of flight testing.

The FSD program began shortly after Hornet's first flight on November 18, 1978 when the aircraft was sent to Patuxent River. During the summer of 1982 the Full Scale Development program ended, completing more than three and a half years of flight testing and performance and systems evaluations. Every effort was made by McAir and the US Navy to put the Hornet through a rigorous and realistic test syllabus, to find potential problems, and correct them before the aircraft entered regular fleet service.

Several problems did show up during the flight test program that required corrective action. The landing gear failure on Hornet 3, the carrier suitability aircraft, presented probably the most notable of these problems. Specifically, the landing gear suffered from a concentration of stress much higher than expected in one of the ancillary links in the landing gear. It was not a structural member, but one of the links that controls the planning of the main gear. The main gear has an axle that is not fixed rigid to the trailing arm, and as it retracts, this axle twists to fold the wheel flat. There is a series of parallel links that run down through the vertical strut and then through a bell crank along the trailing arm, then to the axle and twists the wheel as it retracts. A set of these planning links, it is believed, was suffering a higher level of stress than predicted. The cause of this is due to the amount of shock strut pressure that had to be put into the shock strut to absorb carrier landings.

The change that came about as a result of this problem was a new dual chamber shock strut. This new strut with telescoping action was designed to give more linear progression of stress during touchdown. Follow-up evaluations indicate this update is successful, eliminating the related failure.

Another fix, as these updates and modifications are sometimes called, was the filling in of 80 percent of the leading edge extension (LEX) slots. This was an early fix installed on the F-18 that was required to help reduce drag during high angles of attack. Drag at the approach angle of attack was being magnified by the bleed-over of the low energy turbulent air on the damper surfaces. Filling in all but a small percentage of these slots helped to correct this problem of turbulent air on the damper surfaces.

Originally, the slots in the leading edge extension were a Northrop idea carried over from the YF-17 Cobra. The leading edge extension and slots were designed to put a high energy vortex along each side of the fuselage running back to the fins in order to provide increased directional stability. Unfortunately, the open LEX slots proved to be a bigger penalty in drag than expected.

Another modification that came about as a result of the flight test program at Patuxent River, was the filling in of the snag in the stabilators. The stabilator snag was not carried over from the original Northrop design, but was actually a guess by McAir anticipating a potential flutter problem. McAir based this assumption on previous engineering experience gained during the F-15 development program, which resulted in a similar snag in the F-15's stabilators. But two things happened. First, the flutter problem as anticipated didn't occur. And second, the F-18 was

Four F-18 Hornets in formation over the Chesapeake Bay during the Initial Operational Test and Evaluation program conducted by Navy and Marine personnel. The photograph provides an excellent view of the new straight wing leading edge and filled-in LEX slots.   *(McDonnell Douglas)*

Navy ground personnel prepare to launch this TF-18 from VFA-125. The TF-18 incorporates the same production updates as the single-seat Hornet.   *(Huston)*

Underside view of Hornet 1 in flight.

(McDonnell Douglas)

experiencing a high nose wheel lift-off speed problem. Through engineering studies McAir discovered that more surface area was needed in the stabilators. As a result the stabilator snag was filled in which brought it flush with the remaining stabilator area, and reduced the troublesome nose wheel lift-off speed problem.

The snag in the leading edge of the wing was also removed in an effort to reduce approach speeds and to reduce the effects of turbulent boundary layer air. Instead of filling in the snag as on the stabilators, the wing leading edge snag was actually cut off at the outboard panel. At the same time, other modifications were made to the wing. Originally the wing had a nearly razor sharp leading edge. Since the Hornet was basically a straight-winged aircraft, this sharp leading edge was needed for supersonic flight. But it was this sharp leading edge that caused early separation and forming of turbulent boundary layer air on the top surfaces at carrier approach speeds. To correct this problem McAir shortened the cord of the leading edge flaps and increased the radius of the curvature. In effect, this made the leading edge slightly blunted, but increased drag at slower approach speeds and helped relieve some of the turbulent boundary air on the top surfaces.

Underside view of Hornet 7. Note the differences from number 1 above. In particular, note the addition of ECM fairings under the intakes.

(McDonnell Douglas)

This photo of a Hornet 3 on the USS Carl Vinson shows how eighty percent of the LEX slots were filled in leaving only the one located just below the words Carl Vinson. *(McDonnell Douglas)*

This close-up in-flight view shows several Hornet changes from a different angle. Visible in this photo are the straight leading edge on the wing, the full span aileron, the ECM fairings under the intakes, the filled in LEX slots, and the grill work on the nose.   (McDonnell Douglas)

The biggest and most publicized update in the Hornet during the FSD program had to do with its roll rate problem. The problem was an extremely low roll rate at high subsonic speeds, Mach .95, at low altitudes. The Hornet's wing was exhibiting the same problems the P-51 and F-86 pilots found at transonic speeds. This problem was aileron reversal. However, the Hornet was getting good roll rate in all other aspects.

The fixes came in stages; Roll Rate Mod 1 and Roll Rate Mod 2. Roll Rate Mod 1 was the strengthening of the outboard wing panels with more stiffeners and beefing up the aft spar. The ailerons were increased in size by extending them outward to the wingtip, and also giving differential movement to the trailing edge flaps. Roll Rate Mod 2 gave differential leading edge flap movement by a maximum of plus or minus 3 degrees. This fix unloads the wing and moves the pressure point away from the center of the wing to

help relieve stress. In addition, the flight controls computer software was updated along with the roll rate mods to a point where lateral stick movement controlled almost all hydraulically powered flight controls. "We laugh," said F-18 test pilot LCdr Ken Cockrell in explaining the roll rate mods, "because in lateral stick movement we have leading edge flap, trailing edge flap, aileron, differential stabilator (which is always in effect), and the rudders also deflect slightly to balance flight." "So," continues Cockrell, "there is nothing powered hydraulically that does not move when the stick is moved laterally."

The computer programmed flight controls have been continuously updated coinciding with the progress of the Full Scale Development program. One of these early computer programmed updates came about as a result of the crash of Hornet 12. LCdr C. T. Brannon, a VX-4 pilot participating in the flight test program at Patuxent River, was performing a routine

Hornet 14 with the unsuccessful 315 gallon elliptical drop tank on the centerline station. The spun fibre and aluminum drop tank has been replaced with a conventional cylindrical design.

Close-up of the elliptical drop tank from the front. Also note the slot above and between the splitter plate and fuselage.

test flight when he lost control of the aircraft at about 20,000 feet. Brannon ejected safely from the Hornet before it crashed into the Chesapeake Bay during the November 14, 1980 flight.

However, it took until December 5, nearly four weeks, to duplicate Brannon's uncontrolled flight so that a cause could be found and a fix implemented. The technique used by McAir test pilots to repeat Brannon's uncontrolled flight, using Hornet 6, was described as a high side yo-yo maneuver starting at 300 kt, 22,000 feet, attaining a 50 to 70 degree angle of attack at 250 kt by pulling maximum aft stick and up to 5 g forces on the aircraft. This approximates a flat spin except that the yaw rate is very slow and the Hornet's nose moves up and down in an oscillating manner.

The maneuver was duplicated twice. In the first departure from controlled flight the McAir test pilot was able to regain control by using maximum power on the engine on the inside of the yaw and flight idle on the outside engine.

Prior to the second attempt at this uncontrolled flight problem, a switch was added to the cockpit of Hornet 6 to deactivate the flight control computer giving full lateral authority to the pilot. The pilot then used the full authority of the ailerons in the spin to regain control of the aircraft. McDonnell Douglas, in an attempt to find a solution to the problem, is evaluating reprogramming the flight controls computer to give full lateral authority to the pilot upon sensing uncontrolled flight.

One of the most recent updates has to do with the Hornet's 315 gallon elliptical drop tanks, and this came about as a result, in part, of the carrier suitability trials. The new 315 gallon drop tank was designed specifically for the F-18 Hornet. The basic design theory behind the elliptical tank was to give sufficient ground clearance for the aircraft carrier's catapult mechanism, and to provide a super lightweight tank. The Hornet's elliptical drop tank is made from spun fibre impregnated with aluminum. Unfortunately, failures began to appear due to stress from catapult launches and arrested landings, as well as normal filling and emptying of the fuel. The spun fibre tanks began flexing and were not living up to their expected design life. The resulting change produced a more conventional cylindrical drop tank, simpler in design, stronger, and increased in fuel capacity by 15 gallons to 330 gallons.

The most recent changes that we can report on involves the addition of ECM bumps under the air intakes, flare dispensers next to them, and finally a notch in the aileron. The notched aileron was brand new as of the press date of this book, and the only photo available that showed it is on page 54.

Undoubtedly, the Hornet will undergo many more changes after this book is published. Technology is moving forward at a rapid rate, and the F/A-18 is just now entering operational service. Detail & Scale hopes to produce a follow-up book on the Hornet in a few years that will include its operational usage and any future modifications which are made.

The one and only Convair 880 serving with the U.S. military. Designated UC-880, the Convair is used as an air refueling tanker for the F/A-18 Hornet program at Patuxent River. The former FAA aircraft is operated by Flight Systems International utilizing a KA-3 tanker package.

A recent photograph of a production F-18 on the assembly line. This Hornet incorporates all of the latest changes including full span slotted ailerons, straight leading edges on the wings and stabilators, and filled in LEX slots.

(McDonnell Douglas)

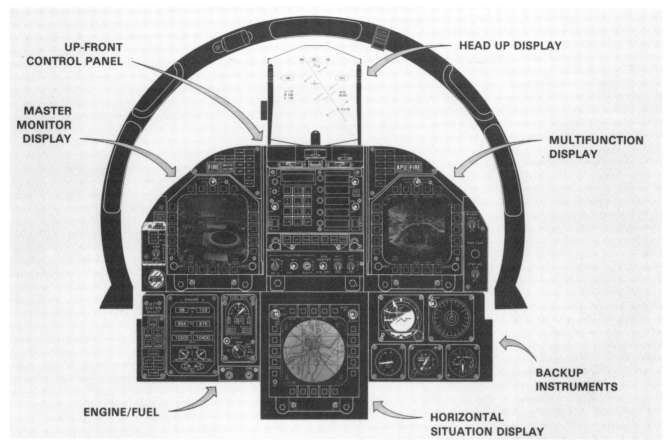

UP-FRONT
CONTROL PANEL

HEAD UP DISPLAY

MASTER
MONITOR
DISPLAY

MULTIFUNCTION
DISPLAY

BACKUP
INSTRUMENTS

ENGINE/FUEL

HORIZONTAL
SITUATION DISPLAY

F-18 updated cockpit layout.

(McDonnell Douglas)

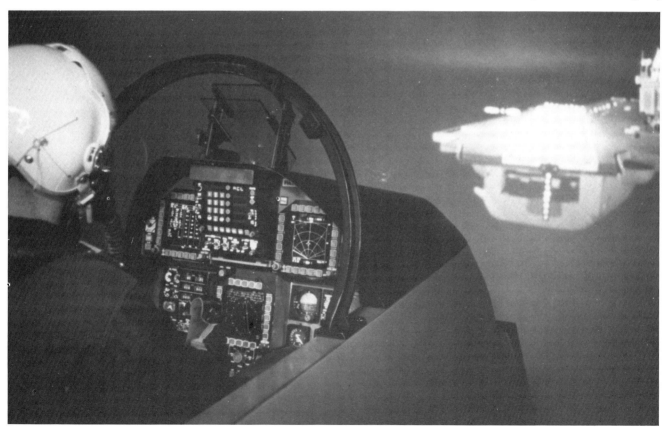

Hornet cockpit simulator provides realistic training for F/A-18 pilots within a domed structure.

(McDonnell Douglas)

TECHNICAL DATA

POWER PLANT

Number and Model	(2) F404-GE-400
Manufacturer	General Electric
Specification:	CP45K0006
Type	Axial Flow Turbofan
Augmentation	Fully Modulated Afterburner (No Stops)
Length with A/B	158.8 in. (Cold)
Inlet Diameter	27.8 in. (Cold)
Dry Weight	2,161 lb.
Tail Pipe	Variable Position CD

RATINGS*

Power Setting (A/B)	
Maximum (A/B)	Static Thrust at Sea Level (lb) 16,000 lb. class
Intermediate	10,000 lb. class

*As defined in G.E. spec CP45K0006, reprinted January 1980, para. 3.2.1.1 Table I and subject to conditions therein.

ELECTRONICS

Airborne Weapons Control	
Radar Set	AN/APG-65
Armament Control-Processor Set	AN/AYQ-9 (V)
Detecting Set	AN/AAS-38
Laser Detector-Tracter-Strike Camera Set	AN/ASQ-173
Electronic Warfare	
Interference Blanker	MX-9965/A
Navigation and Flight Aids	
Inertial Navigation Set	AN/ASN-130
Air Date Computer	CP-1334/A
Signal Data Recording Set	AN/ASM-612
Digital Display Indicator	ID-2150/ASM-612
Communication and Identification	
Control-Converter	C-10382/A
Intercommunication Amplifier-Control	AM-6979/A
Control and Display	
Head-Up Display Unit	AN/AVQ-28
Indicator Group	OD-150 (V)/A
Horizontal Indicator	IP-1350/A
Engine Performance-Crew Station Indicator	AEU-12/A
Motion Picture Camera	KB-34A
Electronic Equipment Control	C-10380/ASQ
Flight Control Set	AN/ASW-44
Electronic Flight Control Set	
Government Furnish Equipment	
Antennas, Radomes, RF Components and Band Suppression Filter	F-1471/ALQ-126
ECM Receiver Set	AN/ALR-45
Electronic Altimeter	RE-1015/APN-194

MISSION AND DESCRIPTION

The F/A-18A will be employed in two mission applications, fighter and attack. When employed in fighter squadrons the F/A-18A will provide for tactical air projection over land and sea and complement Fleet Air Defense. The primary attack missions are interdiction, close air support, defense suppression, strike against seaborne targets, and tactical nuclear strike.

The F/A-18A is a single place, twin tail, twin engine, high performance, aircraft carrier suitable aircraft. The airframe is a balance of conventional and composite materials. External skins for the trailing edge flaps, stabilator, vertical tails, and many access doors are made of graphite composite material. A powered wingfold system minimizes deck area spotting requirements.

Two low by pass turbofan engines with afterburners power the F/A-18A. The internal fuel supply can be supplemented up to three 315-gallon external fuel tanks. A retractable refueling probe provides in-flight refueling capability.

Armament is carried on nine store stations. Two wing tip stations are dedicated to Sidewinders. Lower fuselage stations carry two Sparrows for fighter missions or a Forward Looking IR and Laser Spot Tracker for surface attack missions. The other five wing stations can carry a complement of conventional and precision-guided air-to-surface weapons. The F/A-18A is also equipped with an internal M61 20 mm gun.

The aircraft is controlled by a digital fly-by-wire Flight Control System through irreversible hydraulic flight control surfaces. A mechanical back-up to the stabilator provides get home and land capability even with severe combat damage. Lateral control is provided by a combination of ailerons, flaperons, and asymmetric deflections of the all-movable horizontal tail. Pitch attitude is controlled by symmetric deflections of the horizontal tail. Directional control is provided by dual rudders. High lift devices consist of leading and trailing edge flaps and a fixed leading edge extension to the wing. Maneuvering flaps are used to enhance turn performance. A single speedbrake is located on the upper centerline.

The F/A-18A's multimission capability is due largely to the APG-65 multimode radar. A digital signal processor allows operation in both air-to-air and air-to-surface modes. Air-to-air modes include search, track, and air combat maneuvering automatic acquisition modes. Air-to-surface radar modes include ground mapping, moving target indicator/track, fixed target track, and terrain avoidance. A raid mode which resolves closely spaced airborne targets and a Doppler Beam Sharpened Patch mode with a resolution improvement of 67:1 over the real beam radar map mode are the highlights of the system. Other air-to-air modes include search, track, and air combat maneuvering automatic acquisition modes. Digitally-generated clutter-free radar displays aid the pilot in interpreting the display and analyzing tactical situations.

The avionics system is designed for one-man operation. Two central digital computers interface with the avionics suite which is tied together through a digital multiplex system. Flight and combat information is presented to the pilot on a Head-up Display and three CRT Digital Display Indicators. An Up-front Control located just below the Head-up Display is used to command all communication, navigation, and identification functions. Most weapon system modes can be controlled with switches on the throttle or stick, and during critical attack phases, the pilot need not remove his hands from the throttle and stick.

Other electronics includes radio communication and navigation equipment, an inertial navigation set, an air data computer, and an automatic flight control system. The F/A-18A has a pressurized cabin with an ejection seat, a liquid oxygen system, an anti-G system, and an exposure suit ventilating system.

DIMENSIONS

Wing	
Area	400 sq ft
Span	40.4 ft
M.A.C.	11.52 ft
Sweepback (25% Chord)	20°
Incidence	0°
Dihedral	-3°

Length	56.0 ft
Height	15.3 ft
Wheelbase	17.8 ft
Tread	10.2 ft
MLG Tires	30 x 11.5-14.5 24 PR
NLG Tires	22 x 6.6-10 20 PR

DEVELOPMENT

Contract Date	Dec 75
First Flight	Nov 78
Initial NPE	Mar 79
Initial Carrier Sea Trials	Oct 79
First Flight Pilot Production	Apr 80

WEIGHTS

Aircraft	Loading	lb
F-18A	Empty	21,830
	Basic	22,689
	Combat	31,000
	Design	31,021
F/A-18A	Maximum Takeoff Field	51,900
	Cat.	51,900
A-18A	Maximum Landing Field	39,000
	Arrest	30,700
F/A-18A	Basic Empty	21,858
	Design	24,446
	Basic	31,000
	Combat	40,316

FUEL AND OIL

FUEL		
Location		Gallons
Fuselage, Bladder		1,405
Wing, Integral (Includes Feed Lines)		192
Fuselage, External Drop		315
Wing, External Drop		630
No. Tanks	4	
	2	
	1	
	2	
Grade	JP-4 or JP-5	
Specification	MIL-F-5624B-1	

OIL	
Grade	MIL-L-23699 or MIL-L-7808
Integral with Engines (Usable Tank Capacity per Engine)	1 Gal.

ORDNANCE

6 BBL M61A1 (20 mm) Gun Internally Mounted in Nose, with 400 RDS Ammo

	Armament Stations								
	1	2	3	4	5	6	7	8	9
Air-to-Air Missiles									
Sidewinder (AIM-9G/H/L)	1								1
Sparrow (AIM-7F)				1		1			
Air-to-Ground Missiles									
AGM-65E Maverick		2	2				2	2	
AGM-88 HARM		1	1	1		1	1	1	
Conventional Weapons									
MK-82 LD/FD		2	2	1		1	2	2	
MK-82 LD (Conical Fin)		2	2	1		1	2	2	
MK-82 LGB		2	2				2	2	
MK-83 LD		1	1	1		1	1	1	
MK-83 LGB		1	1				1	1	
MK-84 LD		1	1				1	1	
MK-84 LGB		1	1				1	1	
MK-20 Rockeye II		2	2	1		1	2	2	
CBU-59/B APAM		2	2	1		1	2	2	
BLU-95 FAE-II		2	2				2	2	
WALLEYE I	TBD	TBD			TBD			TBD	TBD
WALLEYE I ER/DL	TBD	TBD			TBD			TBD	TBD
WALLEYE I/L POD					1				
WALLEYE II	TBD	TBD			TBD			TBD	TBD
WALLEYE II ER/DL	TBD	TBD			TBD			TBD	TBD
Practice Bombs									
MK-106		2	2	1		1	2	2	
MK-76		2	2	1		1	2	2	
BDU-12/20		2	2	1		1	2	2	
BDU-36		2	2	1		1	2	2	
Rocket Packages									
LAU-10D/A		2	2				2	2	
LAU-61A/A		2	2				2	2	
LAU-68B/A		2	2				2	2	
Special Weapons									
B-57		1	1				1	1	
B-61		1	1				1	1	

VX-4

Hornets assigned to VX-4, one of the Navy's evaluation squadrons.

(McDonnell Douglas)

A VX-4 F-18 sporting a Playboy bunny on its rudder.

(Cockle)

VFA-125

VFA-125, the first Hornet squadron, was commissioned on 13 November 1980 at NAS Lemoore. Tail stripes are green. *(McDonnell Douglas/Yarbrough)*

The first Hornet squadron, VFA-125 "The Rough Riders," was officially formed on 13 November 1980 at NAS Lemoore, California. The ceremonies were complete with an F-18 (s/n 161216), borrowed from the flight test program at Patuxent River, painted with grey NJ tailcodes and dark green rudder stripes. But these ceremonies were more than celebrating of the commissioning of the first Hornet squadron. It put the F/A-18 another step closer to front line service with the fleet.

The mission of VFA-125 as a replacement training squadron, is to train new F/A-18 pilots and maintenance personnel for fleet squadrons. Initially however, VFA-125 is tasked with training the first F/A-18 instructor pilots and support personnel who, in turn, will train the pilots and enlisted personnel for the Hornet squadrons to follow.

Nine instructor pilot trainees began training in the Hornet in March 1981, with seven more instructor pilot trainees joining "The Rough Riders" by the following August. A total of 30 Marine and Navy pilots will perform the task of transition training for the first Hornet squadrons to be commissioned in mid-1982. The initial group of instructor pilots represent an even cross section of pilots from both fighter and attack squadrons in the Navy and Marines, with a broad spectrum of experience in such aircraft as the

F-14 and F-4 fighters, and A-4, A-6, and A-7 attack aircraft.

Also responsible for training maintenance personnel as well as pilots, the first group of maintenance people, senior Navy and Marine enlisted men, began their indoctrination in January 1981. Senior enlisted personnel were sought due to their experience level, and they in turn will train younger and less experienced maintenance personnel at the squadron level.

The personnel roster of VFA-125 is nearly evenly divided between Navy and Marine officers and enlisted personnel with Navy Captain Jim Partington as C.O., and Marine LtCol Gary Vangysel as X.O, thus emphasizing the Hornet's dual fighter-attack mission for both services. The squadron is well integrated without division between Navy or Marine personnel, all operating cohesively as a team.

Following "The Rough Riders" November 1980 commissioning at NAS Lemoore, time was spent on administrative organization while waiting for the arrival of the squadron's first Hornets. Finally, on 19 February 1981, "The Rough Riders" received their first F/A-18. It was one of the Hornets originally assigned to VX-4, and it joined the squadron's two A-7E Corsairs. The A-7s are utilized as air intercept targets, target tow aircraft, and perform other duties

An F-18 and a TF-18 from VFA-125 fly formation. As a training squadron, VFA-125 operates a lot of TF-18s. (McDonnell Douglas)

Two flying views of a VFA-125 Hornet showing the gray NJ tail code and stencilling. (McDonnell Douglas)

One of two A-7E Corsairs attached to VFA-125 in formation with one of the "Rough Riders" F/A-18s. The Corsairs are used as intercept targets as well as target tow aircraft. (McDonnell Douglas)

TF-18 during January 1982 deployment to Yuma where Hornets participated in 23 days of Air Combat Maneuvering exercises. (Huston)

as required.

The Hornet delivered to VFA-125 in February, and the two subsequent Hornets that followed, were pilot production aircraft. The first full scale production Hornet was delivered in September 1981. Five additional production Hornets were delivered by the end of 1981. However, the number of aircraft will grow considerably during the next four years with the squadron expected to be operating 60 Hornets, at its peak, with more than 600 personnel.

A few minor problems did occur during September resulting in a decrease in the number of monthly flight hours. Previously, the squadron was averaging 50 flight hours per airplane per month for the first six months of flight operations. But leaking fuel cells caused a decrease in the number of flight hours. In fact the squadron had experienced three fuel cell changes during September. The cause was traced back to improper fuel cell testing prior to installation in the aircraft. However, revised testing procedures have corrected this problem.

During February 1981 "The Rough Riders" left NAS Lemoore for the squadron's first extended deployment. Nine F-18 and TF-18 Hornets deployed to Marine Corps Air Station, Yuma, for 23 days of Air Combat Maneuvering exercises against U.S. and Canadian fighter squadrons.

Ground tracking station computers monitored the flights allowing kills to be confirmed using data transmitted from the aircraft. Reportedly Hornets routinely gained the advantage during these encounters. The Hornet's performance proved greater than expected during this deployment to Yuma permitting the original flight schedule of 288 missions to be increased by 13 percent to 326 sorties. More than 400 flight hours were accumulated by the Hornets during their 23 days at Yuma.

With the experience gained from their deployments, and the tactics developed, VFA-125 instructors will be well prepared to train the new Hornet pilots to come. The training syllabus for new F/A-18 pilots is expected to last about six months. Maintenance personnel training is expected to take four to five months.

Pilots will be dual qualified after receiving both air-to-air and air-to-ground training. The six month long flight syllabus for new pilots assigned to VFA-125 will involve 69 sorties and 86 flying hours for familiarization with the F/A-18 and its systems. Carrier qualifications will require an additional 20 sorties and 22 flying hours.

The pilots of VFA-125 are finding their new Hornets to be more than previously expected. They report the transition to the F/A-18 to be easy, identifying cockpit layout and ease of systems operations as the reasons. Others report the F-18, in air combat training, has greater fuel endurance than the F-14 Tomcat. Former A-7 pilots, in comparing the Hornet's performance, claim the A-7 has slightly greater range than the Hornet, but lacks the power of the Hornet, something attack pilots have always wanted.

The Marines received their first Hornets in July 1982 at NAS Lemoore. VMFA-323 and VMFA-531 will transition from their F-4J/S Phantoms to Hornets. The first Navy squadrons to transition will be VA-146 and VA-147, both based at NAS Lemoore, when they trade in the A-7E Corsairs in 1983-84. A total of 40 Hornet squadrons are scheduled from both the Navy and Marines from the 1,377 F/A-18 Hornets currently on order with McDonnell Douglas.

"The Rough Riders" squadron commander, Captain Jim Partington's Hornet on the ramp at MCAS Yuma, January 1982.

(Huston)

RF-18

One of the proposed configurations for the Hornet includes cameras in the nose and a reconnaissance pod system. *(McDonnell Douglas)*

In 1979 the Navy's primary shipboard photo reconnaissance aircraft, the RA-5C Vigilante, was retired from service as a victim of old age. The Vigilante was a modification to an existing airframe as is the case with other Navy photo recce aircraft. In the case of the Vigilante it was modified for the recon role by converting the bomb bay from carrying bombs to carrying a full array of reconnaissance sensing equipment. But the key to the Vigilante's conversion to a photo reconnaissance aircraft was its availability. It came about as Navy policy changes in 1962 abandoned the role of strategic bombing, a role the Vigilante was specifically designed for. As a result of this major shift in Navy policy, the Vigilante was soon out of work, but not for long. Navy planners saw the potential benefits of the Vigilante as a photo reconnaissance asset. The rest is history.

The retirement of the Vigilante left the RF-8 Crusader as the Navy's primary photo recce asset, and like the Vigilante, the RF-8 Crusader was based on an existing airframe. But again, like the Vigilante, the Crusader is suffering from old age and is due to be transferred to the Navy Reserves in 1982.

To fill the void left by the retiring of the Navy's main photo recce assets is the Marine Corps' RF-4 Phantom and the Navy's new F-14 TARPS Tomcats. Sometimes referred to as the "Peeping Tom," the new F-14 TARPS entered fleet service in 1980 with VF-124, and will serve as an interim measure until the 1990s, or when a new photo recce aircraft can be developed.

Thirty-six new F-14 TARPS (TARPS being an acronym for Tactical Airborne Reconnaissance Pod System) were constructed specifically to carry a new camera/infrared sensor pod on the aircraft's number 5 Phoenix missile station. Moreover, these new TARPS Tomcats can easily be converted to regular F-14 fighters, but regular F-14s cannot be converted

to TARPS. Currently, Navy plans call for 2 or 3 F-14 TARPS Tomcats to be deployed in conjunction with regular F-14s in fleet squadron service on board carriers, giving air group commanders the option of having a photo recce asset built into their fighter squadrons.

All this leads to the potential for a new RF-18 Hornet to fill the void left by the RF-8 Crusader and the RA-5 Vigilante. Funding has been approved for design feasibility studies to explore the possibility of converting the F/A-18 to a photo recce version utilizing its existing airframe and without the need for major changes.

Several design proposals have been introduced, either in a complete conversion to an RF-18, or by merely carrying a camera pod similar to the F-14 TARPS. Both single and two-seat Hornet configurations are under consideration. The two-seat Hornet configuration was an early proposal. Camera layout and backseat controls and functions closely followed the same basic format as the RF-4 Phantom. This proposed transformation to photo reconnaissance is straightforward utilizing the TF-18 airframe. The major change would be to remove the Hornet's GAU-11 gun system and replace it with various sensors. A new lower fuselage section is envisioned to house the camera windows. This would give the lower fuselage a slightly bulged appearance just aft of the nose cone. Various framing and panoramic cameras, infrared, and data systems recorders could be installed to give the Hornet complete photo recce capability.

The single-seat photo Hornet is based on the same design principle as the two-seat version, and it has greater potential for acceptance by the Navy. The unique feature developed with the newer proposed single-seat configuration is the palletized reconnaissance system. Theoretically, by making a few changes to the GAU-11 gun location, which is also palletized and loaded into the aircraft through an access door in the lower fuselage, the palletized reconnaissance pod system could be installed in place of the GAU-11 gun system. To carry this proposal further, consideration is being given to building a given number of F/A-18s that would have this convertible feature. These aircraft would be able to convert from fighter/attack to photo reconnaissance by replacing the palletized gun system with a palletized photo reconnaissance system. This would be similar to the convertibility of the F-14 TARPS. Moreover, it would mean an immediate benefit to air group commanders in having a built-in photo recce asset within the fighter/attack squadrons, thus eliminating the need for a separate photo reconnaissance aircraft.

No definite plan to implement any of these proposals is evident at press time. But it is a viable alternative to the Navy's need for a new photo reconnaissance asset, and would further enhance the Hornet's versatility.

MODELER'S SECTION

PRODUCT REVIEW POLICY. In each of our publications we will try to review kits and decals that are available to the scale modeler. We hope to be able to review every currently available kit that is useable by the scale modeler. Kits produced in the past that are no longer generally available, and those more intended to be toys than accurate scale models will not usually be covered. Additionally, we do not intend to give a complete step-by-step, correction-by-correction account of how to build each kit. Instead we intend to give a brief description of what is available to the modeler, and point out some of the good and not-so-good points of each kit or product. In this way we hope to give an overall picture of what the modeler has readily available for his use in building the particular aircraft involved.

KIT REVIEWS

LS/Otaki 1/144th Scale F-18

A nice kit for its size, but it may be regarded by most modelers as falling within the toy category and not really suited for the serious modeler. However, it is an accurate model of the Hornet, within scale dimensions, and easy to build.

Consisting of 25 parts, the molding features petite scribed detail. The landing gear tends to be a little delicate, not surprising in this small scale, but is accurate and captures the look of the real Hornet. The cockpit area is void of any detail. The one-piece canopy is crisp and clear. There is no test pitot boom included, but in this small scale a bit of stretched sprue should do as a substitute.

Decals are of good quality featuring markings for Hornet 1, but lacking the blue and gold trim. The national insignia on the wings seems a bit undersized. All-in-all this is not a bad little kit, and it builds up into an attractive and accurate model of the Hornet.

Hasegawa/Minicraft 1/72nd Scale F-18

Excellent molding with raised panel line detail and engraved flight controls highlight this 52 piece kit of the F-18. Overall shape and outline are well defined, with basic scale dimensions very close. Accurately detailed landing gear, with interior detail molded into the wheel wells and inside of the landing gear doors, are included. Also provided in this kit is an optionally positioned air brake which fits very well opened or closed. Overall fit and ease of assembly of this kit is rated at good to excellent.

The two-piece ejection seat is joined vertically down the middle of the seat causing a little work for the builder to remove the resulting seam. The Sparrow missile mounts are molded into the side of the fuselage and are not optional which leaves a bit of a problem if you wish to build this F-18 without Sparrow missiles. Another minor problem concerns the long pitot test boom. When this kit was originally released by Hasegawa in Japan, it included decals for Hornet 1 for which the long test boom is correct and very well done. However, Minicraft, in releasing this kit in this country, has opted for decals made by Scalemaster of prototype number 3 which has no test boom. If modelling the number 3 prototype, the carrier qualification Hornet, you must break off the long pitot test boom at its base and then sand the nose

The winner in its class at the 1981 IPMS/USA National Convention was this 1/72nd scale Hornet from Minicraft, highly detailed by its builder, Buzz Lockwood.

cone to shape. Or, disregard the kit test boom and fill in the attachment hole left in the nose cone with putty and sand smooth, saving the test boom for another Hornet. This is a minor disadvantage to an otherwise excellent kit.

The cockpit is well done with side consoles molded to the floor, and a very accurate control stick is also included. The ejection seat, as previously mentioned, is molded in two pieces and presents a reasonably accurate seat. The canopy is very clean and crisply molded in two pieces allowing the finished model to be displayed with either open or closed canopy.

Two Sparrow missiles and two Sidewinder missiles are the only ordnance included in this kit, which is one of the best in 1/72nd scale.

Entex 1/72nd Scale F-18

We feel there is no need to give a lengthy review of this kit as it is generally no longer available in most areas. This was the first of the F-18 kits released, and is not very accurate in detail. However it is reasonably accurate in scale.

The fit is really bad, and requires a good deal of putty around all major seams, especially the wing roots. The decals, on the other hand, are of good quality with markings for Hornet 1, and a good looking instrument panel decal is included. But when considering the effort needed to build this kit, and taking into account the quality of the other Hornet kits now available, your efforts would be better spent elsewhere.

Testors-Italeri 1/72nd Scale F-18/TF-18

The molding of this 82 piece kit is excellent, with

superb, well detailed landing gear, which is by far the most accurate in this scale. Overall size and shape are very accurate, and with the option for building a single-seat or two-seat F-18, we consider this kit to be the best 1/72nd scale kit of the Hornet.

Surface detail of delicate raised panel lines and engraved flying surfaces are well done. The interior of the wheel wells, and the detail molded to the inside of the landing gear doors, all add to the realism of this kit.

Cockpit detail is excellent. Two one-piece ejection seats are included, due to the TF-18 option, along with two accurately molded control sticks. The instrument panels for both front and back seats are also included, with side consoles for each molded onto the cockpit floor. Also under cockpit detail is the option to have the canopy either opened or closed in both the F-18 and TF-18 configurations. The canopy pieces are clear and accurately molded. The one problem worth making note of is the assembly of the vertical fins, parts 26 and 27, to the fuselage. Care must be taken here to get the proper alignment.

Additional extra detail is the optional fuselage mounts for the two Sparrow missiles. The wingtip Sidewinder missile rails are molded separately, as are the trailing edge flap hinges. A pair of inaccurately shaped drop tanks, something none of the kit manufacturers seem to have right, are added, as well as extra pylons and ejector racks for four Mk.83 bombs.

Microscale decals are provided with markings for the first TF-18, Hornet 3, and for the markings applied to the F-18 used in the commissioning ceremonies for the new F-18 training squadron VFA-125. However, as the Hornet used for the VFA-125 commissioning ccremony represents one of the early production F-18s, the builder will need to make the appropriate modifications, such as filling in the leading edge extension (LEX) slots, and removing the snag in the wing leading edge, Italeri has already added one early modification by eliminating the notch in the stabilator.

Other extra details in this kit, such as the two sets of exhaust nozzles, well defined fuselage mounted pitot tubes, the quality of the molding with a very good fit of the parts, and the ability to build two versions, all add to make this kit our number one pick in 1/72nd scale.

Scale Craft/ESCI 1/72nd Scale F-18

This is a much improved version over ESCI's previously released 1/48th scale kit and truer to scale. But, again this is another kit of the prototype Hornet lacking any of the early production changes. Molded in white plastic of 60 pieces, plus a crisp two-piece canopy, kit molding features raised panel lines and engraved flight controls including a good representation of the wing folding mechanism. Cockpit interior is well done with side consoles molded to the cockpit floor. But there is a minor problem with the cockpit floor being slightly too wide requiring some trimming with a hobby knife to fit properly. There was also a twist, due to warping, in the nose area of part 7A, the upper fuselage section.

The landing gear is well done with good detail for the wheels, and the landing gear doors have interior detail added. Wing tip-mounted AIM-9 Sidewinder missiles are included as are fuselage-mounted AIM-7

Sparrow missiles. No other weapons are included.

Decals of good quality are included for either Hornet 5 or Hornet 6, the orange trimmed spin test aircraft. However, a point worth keeping in mind if modeling Hornet 6 is the lack of the long pitot test boom in this kit, forcing the model builder to scratch build the long test boom from stretched sprue, or take the test boom from another kit.

The two-piece canopy, although crisply molded, is a scaled down version from the 1/48th scale kit with the same bulged look to the roof of the canopy, although it is not as noticeable in this smaller scale.

Overall fit of this kit is fair with the exception of the warped nose section as already noted. The overall size and outline are fairly accurate. Moreover, with the few problems being corrected, this kit builds up into a presentable replica of the F-18 Hornet.

Monogram 1/72nd Scale SNAP-TITE F-18

Being a no-glue Snap-Tite kit may cause some model builders to overlook this kit of the Hornet as not being suitable for the serious model builder. But this is a nice kit, very close to scale, accuate, and easy to put together.

Surface detail is well represented by raised panel lines, although the flying surfaces tend to be a little on the heavy side. The landing gear is well done and looks good on the finished model. The nose area appears to be a little too straight, or flat, not having enough curve to it, but this isn't a major problem.

Decals are of good quality featuring Hornet 3, the carrier suitability aircraft. However, the decals are slightly inaccurate in that the blue trim is a little too

Monogram publicity photograph of their F-18 Snap-Tite kit in 1/72nd scale.   **(Monogram)**

ESCI 1/48th Scale Hornet finished in the markings of VF-72 by Joe Smith.

light, and the gold trim for the stabilators is missing.

Scale Craft/ESCI 1/48th Scale F-18

This was the first kit of the F-18 to be released, and as such, represents one of the early prototypes. Its profile and size are close to scale, although the wing is slightly oversized in span by 1 scale foot, and it is undersized in length by 2½ scale feet.

Molded in a light gray plastic and consisting of 77 parts, this kit features raised panel line detail. The landing gear are well defined, and the landing gear doors have interior detail added. The fit can best be described as fair. We found in our review sample part number 21B, lower rear fuselage section, to be slightly warped. If not corrected before hand, this will cause a poor fit of the main wheel wells, part numbers 43C & 44C, and will result in an incorrect sitting attitude of the finished model. However, as this was one of the first kits released, this problem may have been corrected in subsequent production runs.

Cockpit detail is sparse with only a floor with molded side consoles and a separate instrument panel provided. The ejection seat is very basic, but can easily be detailed by the more experienced model builder. The cockpit area is easily viewed through the

crisply molded two-piece canopy with plenty of room for extra detail. The canopy itself, however, appears inaccurate in outline, having a slightly bulged look to the roof of the canopy near the canopy-windscreen separation.

Weapons included in this kit are two wing tip-mounted AIM-9 Sidewinder missiles and four Mk.82 low drag bombs. Two 315 gallon drop tanks are provided, but should be discarded as they bear little resemblance to the elliptical drop tanks as used on the prototype aircraft.

Decals supplied with the kit provide only US national insignia, some stencilling, and jet intake warning triangles. No serial numbers or prototype markings are included. Instead ESCI, as their boxtop artwork indicates, opted for a "provisional" all gray scheme which to date no F-18 has appeared in.

Taking the few minor problems with this kit into consideration, and making the necessary corrections, it can be built into a reasonably accurate F-18 prototype.

Revell 1/48th Scale F-18 Hornet

Revell has released two separate 1/48th scale kits of the F-18, and although they are essentially the same kit, they can be built In two different versions. The first release, kit number 4500, is of the first F-18 prototype with appropriate markings. The second release, kit number 4505, represents an F-18 from VF-11 with a compliment of under-wing stores not found in the previous release. However, it should be noted that these markings are totally inaccurate as VF-11, at the time of this writing, has begun transitioning from F-4J Phantoms to F-14 Tomcats, and will probably never fly F-18s.

Since both kits are basically the same, the following kit review will be the same for each. Kit 4500 is 68 parts molded in white plastic. Kit 4505 also contains 68 parts, plus an additional 30 parts for the extra under-wing stores, molded in light gray plastic. Both kits have two Sidewinder and two Sparrow missiles. The one-piece canopy is flash free and clear without distortion. The quality of the molding is good with fine raised panel lines and engraved speed brake detail and flying surfaces to represent surface detail.

Cockpit detail is sparse when compared to the other 1/48th scale kits, with the top of the nose wheel well, part 38, making up the cockpit floor. Part 39 is a single piece containing side consoles and main instrument panel, with decals for each provided in place of raised or engraved detail to represent the flight instruments. A one-piece ejection seat of undetermined type is included.

Overall shape is accurate and dimensions are close to scale. Fit of the kit is good, although the intakes (parts 7 & 8) need a little work to fit properly. The landing gear can be a little complicated to put together.

Decals for kit 4500 represent the number 1 prototype and are of good quality. The markings for this version provide only the basics, requiring the builder to paint the distinctive blue and gold stripes. Also, there is a minor error in these markings in that the word NAVY is repeated on both sides of the fuselage instead of NAVY on the left and MARINES on the right. The VF-11 decals for kit 4505 are completely fictitious.

Testors-Italeri 1/48th Scale F-18/TF-18 Hornet

Molded in 101 pieces of white plastic, this kit is almost the same as its 1/72nd scale brother. Moreover, just as the 1/72nd scale kit is the only one in that scale to provide optional parts to build a TF-18 Hornet, so too, this 1/48th scale kit is the only one within its scale to provide optional parts for the two-seat Hornet.

Overall shape and dimensions are accurate and true to scale, with engraved panel lines and flying surfaces representing surface detail. The cockpit interior is well done with two one-piece ejection seats, two very nice control sticks, cockpit floor with molded side consoles, and two instrument panels. The instrument panels and side consoles have no engraved or raised surface detail added to represent flight instruments. Instead, decals are provided in their place.

The snag, present in the stabilators, is absent here, and reflects one of the early production updates. But the snag, or step, in the wing leading edge is still present, as are the slots in the leading edge extension.

Two sets of exhaust nozzles are included, giving the modeler the option of displaying this model with open or closed exhaust nozzles. Four under-wing pylons are provided with two drop tanks along with two Sidewinder and two Sparrow missiles. Also included is a separate speed brake that can be displayed extended or closed. Two-piece canopies for both versions are crisp and clear without distortion.

The biggest error with this kit appears not in its molded parts, but in its box art. The box top features a completed model of a TF-18 Hornet in the markings of the number 7 prototype which is a single-seat F-18! Following this error in the box art is an even more serious error in kit decals by Microscale. The kit decals provide standard prototype markings for the #3, #7 and T 1 (the first TF-18) Hornets. However, serial number 160782 for the #7 prototype is missing, only serials for #3 and T 1 are included. Moreover, in an effort to provide alternate markings for either a TF-18 or F-18 in the three tone gray camouflage scheme of the early production Hornets, Microscale simply repeated these same decals in subdued gray markings which is not correct for these particular F-18s. Thus the only Hornets that can be accurately modeled from this decal sheet is #3, serial 160777, and TF 1, serial 160781, both in prototype markings.

From a construction point of view this kit goes together well with a few exceptions. There is a little work to be done in fitting the intakes to the lower fuselage section. Likewise, the undersides of the leading edge extension (parts 19 & 21) are slightly warped needing some filling and sanding to fit. But the completed kit, whether F-18 or TF-18, builds into a suitably accurate Hornet. Just be careful to avoid the inaccurate decals.

Monogram 1/48th Scale F-18 Hornet

The cockpit interior in this 91 piece kit, molded in white plastic, is one of the best we have seen in any scale, and is the highlight of this kit. An extremely well detailed four-piece ejection seat, along with the accurate detail molding of the instrument panel, all assembled to a cockpit floor with molded side consoles, makes into a very realistic looking Hornet

Minicraft 1/32nd scale Hornet, finished in the marking of VF-11 and modified to early production standards by builder Paul Kopcynski, is rated as the best Hornet available in kit form.

cockpit.

The overall shape and outline of this kit is accurate with the exception of the nose cone which appears to be too blunt. Scale dimensions are quite accurate. Surface detail features raised panel lines, and in some areas raised rivet detail, with engraved flying surfaces. The area behind the ejection seat is well defined and like that of the real F-18. The speed brake can be assembled in the open or closed position, while the stabilators, when assembled to the fuselage, can be positioned in various attitudes. A crystal-clear two-piece canopy is also included. Two wing tip-mounted Sidewinder missiles, two fuselage-mounted Sparrow missiles (an optional feature), plus two additional Sparrows on under-wing pylons, and a centerline drop tank make up the ordnance and stores. However, the drop tank is inaccurate, and is best discarded.

Fit of the kit is good, but with all the excellent surface detail, there is a problem. The basic assembly of this kit is in two halves; the upper and lower fuselage sections. There appears to have been a tooling problem with the molds, noticeable in the nose area of the lower fuselage section. All the fine surface detail abruptly stops at a mold line that runs at about an eight degree angle from the bottom of the nose to the leading edge extension, where above this line there is no surface detail at all. We can only guess that the original molds did not have the proper contour when joined to the upper fuselage section, and in making the corrections in the molds this problem developed. The result is a slight gap in joining the two fuselage sections together, and this requires filling

and sanding to look right. But, with all things considered, the quality of the remaining molding, the attention to detail, and the overall appeal of the finished model, by far outweighs this problem.

Good quality decals for the number 1 prototype are included with all the blue and gold striping needed for the final finish on an overall glossy white F-18.

Minicraft/Hasegawa 1/32nd Scale F-18 Hornet

The molding of this big and impressive model of the F-18 by Minicraft is excellent, with over 110 pieces included in white plastic. The cockpit detail is the real eyecatcher here. A cockpit floor is provided with highly detail molded side consoles, while the main instrument panel (part D 16) is very authentic looking with molded raised detail to represent flight instruments. Separate rudder pedals, throttle, and a well detailed five-piece ejection seat top off this realistic Hornet cockpit. Surface detail is well defined with fine raised panel lines and engraved flying surfaces.

Overall fit, especially when considering its size and all the seams that have to be worked on, is rated at good to excellent. There are very few problem areas except for the intakes which may require some filling. But in general this kit goes together rather well.

Optional parts add to the appeal of this kit. The two-piece canopy is crisp and clear, the speed brake can be positioned extended or closed, and the cockpit boarding ladder can be displayed extended from the leading edge extension. However, with the exception of the two Sparrow and two Sidewinder missiles, no other weapons are included. Decals by Scalemaster provide markings for the first three prototypes, with the blue and gold trim for Hornet 1 included.

The finished model is exceptional, and with the excellent cockpit interior, the quality of the molding and the attention to detail, we recommend this kit as the best overall F-18 in any scale.

Revell 1/32nd Scale F-18 Hornet

Released in late 1981, Revell's 1/32nd scale Hornet is very much like their previously released 1/48th scale Hornet. With a few exceptions, namely additional parts, this latest release from Revell of the Hornet is essentially a scaled-up version of the 1/48th scale kit. Molded in 108 pieces of light gray plastic, Revell's new Hornet features engraved and raised panel lines to represent surface detail, with engraved flying surfaces. A one-piece canopy is also included.

Accurate in scale, we found only a few minor problems with this kit. The most notable of these is a warped wing (part number 45), which we believe is the exception rather than the rule with this kit. Assembly is easy and straight forward, requiring only a small amount of filling along the fuselage seams.

The cockpit detail, in our opinion, is a little sparse for a model of this size. Similar to the 1/48th scale Hornet, the cockpit utilizes the upper surface of the nose wheel well as the cockpit floor, while the instrument panel, side consoles, and the rear cockpit wall are molded in one piece. Instruments on the main instrument panel, and control knobs and instruments on the side consoles, are represented by molded raised detail. The ejection seat is well done, and helps to add realism to the cockpit.

The landing gear is also very nice, although a little complex. For example, just one of the main landing gear consist of 10 parts, which include rubber tires that are very realistic looking on the finished model. Interior detail to the landing gear wheel wells and gear doors is minimal. Sparrow missiles are the only optional parts included in this kit, while Sidewinder missiles are the only other weapons included. Bombs and drop tanks are not included.

Decals are of good quality, but as in the 1/48th scale kit, they are for a Hornet serving with VF-11 in subdued markings. This is inaccurate. The serial numbers are for the number 3 prototype Hornet.

The finished model, except for its inaccurate decals, is impressive and looks good, being faithful in appearance to the real Hornet.

It is relatively easy to convert the existing Hornet kits, which all represent prototype F-18s, to production Hornets featuring the latest production updates and modifications that have appeared to date. These production updates can be accomplished using the same basic method as did McDonnell Douglas on the actual aircraft. This conversion can also be accomplished without the need for major surgery or additions to the kits and require only a small amount of hobby putty, a bit of trimming, and minor rescribing of panel lines. Beginning on the next page, we explain how to make these changes, not only for this kit, but for all F-18 kits issued to date.

NOTE: At press time for this book, no specialty decal sheets for the F-18 kits had been released. Therefore there are no decal reviews in this book.

Revell 1/32nd scale F-18.

(Revell)

BUILDING A PRODUCTION HORNET

Five areas will require your attention: the LEX slots, stabilators, wing leading edge, ailerons, and the lower fuselage. We recommend using the scale drawings in this book as a guide in completing these updates.

The first, and easiest, of these production updates to complete is the filling in of the snag on the leading edge of the two stabilators. Not all of the kits have this snag, but for the kits that do simply cut a piece of plastic card (the thickness is determined by whatever scale you are working in) to match the thickness of the existing part and glue it in place. Some body putty may be needed to get an even surface appearance.

The second update needed to bring your Hornet kit up to production standards is to fill in 80 percent of the open slots in the leading edge extension on either side of the fuselage. Keep in mind that not all of the open slot area is filled in as has been reported in other publications. The method used in determining how much of the slot area to fill in is to measure approximately 5/8th inch, for 1/72nd scale kits, from the rear wall of the last slot, forward to a point even with the boundary layer bleed grills molded onto the leading extension of most kits. The slot area from this point forward is filled in. For 1/48th scale kits measure 7/8th inch, and for 1/32nd scale kits measure 1-3/8th inch.

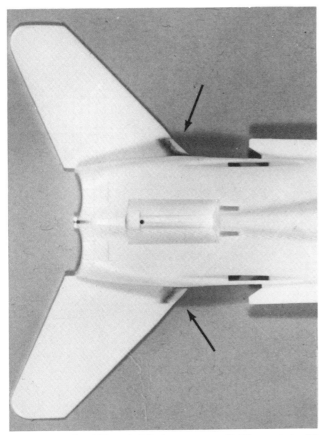

Photograph of the stabilators on an F-18 model with the snag filled in.

The method for filling in the LEX slots will be determined by the scale you are working in, but for the most part hobby putty is recommended. Also, keep in mind when filling in the LEX slots that the remaining portion of the open slot goes all the way through the leading edge extension, exiting between the fuselage and the intake splinter plate, and is on a forward sweep at about a twenty-one degree angle. Finally, after filling in the LEX slots, be sure the filled in area is flush on both top and bottom sides maintaining a good aerodynamic surface.

The next step is to take out the snag in the wing leading edge; and we will proceed using the same basic method as did McDonnell Douglas on the actual aircraft. Instead of simply filling in the snag as on the stabilators, resulting in a wider wing, McAir elected to remove it entirely from the wing. Use the sketch as a reference guide. It should be noted that when removing the snag, the wing cord or width will be reduced by a small amount. In addition the leading edge does not have the same razor sharp edge, but is slightly blunted instead.

To complete this update, measure approximately 1/16th inch, for 1/72nd scale, on the leading edge at a point near the wing root. This is simply a reference point to use with your metal ruler or straight edge. Now take the metal ruler, or straight edge, and place it on the 1/16th inch mark so that it is parallel with the wing leading edge. Next take a sharp pencil or very fine point marking pen and draw a line from the wing root to the wing tip, remove the metal ruler and check to be sure this line does not intersect the wing fold mechanism molded onto the wing. If it does simply erase the line and move it forward, closer to the leading edge and redraw the line. Refer to the sketch to be sure your line is in the correct place. Now that you have verified your line is correctly drawn, place the metal ruler back on the wing to use as a straight edge. Take a sharp hobby knife, and using the metal ruler as a straight edge, begin making gentle cuts along this line. Take your time and be careful not to apply too much pressure cutting this line which may cause you to slip and score the surrounding wing surface area. And be careful not to cut off the Sidewinder missile launcher rails molded onto the wing tips of some kits. Continue making gentle cuts with your hobby knife until you break through the plastic. After cutting through the plastic clean up the cut edge with a file, bringing back the leading edge to a sharp edge, not razor sharp, but slightly blunted.

Now direct your attention to the Hornet's undersides. Just forward of the nose wheel landing gear door are two new grills added to the production Hornet. Refer to our scale drawings for exact location. These are best represented by first drawing the

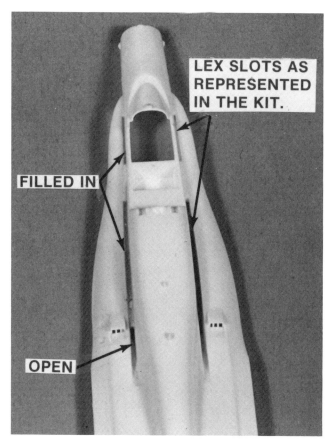

LEX SLOTS AS REPRESENTED IN THE KIT.

FILLED IN

OPEN

This photo is looking down on the top of an F-18 model. The slots on the left LEX have been filled in with the dark colored putty as indicated. The LEX slots on the right side are open as they come in the kit.

grills onto your model to be sure of correct placement, then scribe in the grill frames and grill work with a sharp No. 11 Xacto blade. Moving aft on the Hornet's undersides are two ECM blisters, under each intake, that are easily duplicated on your model with hobby putty. Adjacent to the ECM blisters are two chaff dispensers. Again refer to the scale drawings for exact location. The best method for reproducing the chaff dispensers is to scribe the dispenser frame with a No. 11 Xacto blade.

The last step in updating your Hornet to production standards is to extend the ailerons all the way to the end of the wingtip. Start by carefully filling in the outboard engraved line representing the outboard edge of the ailerons, and sand smooth taking care not to remove surrounding surface detail. Then rescribe the aileron hinge line all the way to the wingtip. Use a metal straight edge and a sharp hobby knife following the existing aileron hinge line, continuing it to the wing tip. Be careful not to apply too much pressure which may cause an accidental slip damaging the wing surface. Be sure to complete the same on the bottom of the wing.

If you desire to have the notched ailerons, simply cut out the notch after extending the ailerons as described above. Refer to our scale drawings as a reference for the notch.

Following all of these modifications, you now have an early production Hornet. These same updates also apply to the TF-18 Hornet.

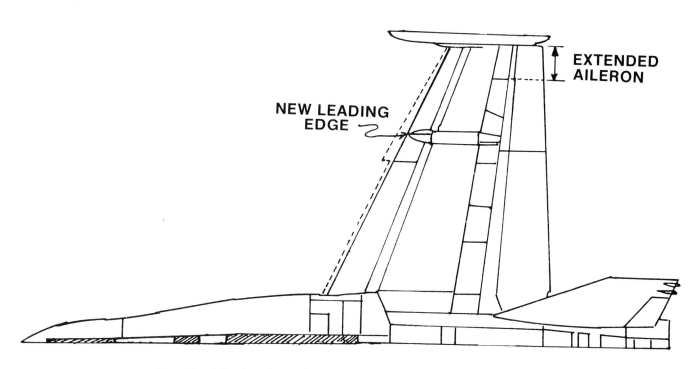

EXTENDED AILERON

NEW LEADING EDGE

Sketch of the leading edge and extended aileron modifications.

MODELERS • COLLECTORS • HISTORIANS
MILITARY ENTHUSIASTS • AVIATION BUFFS
SCHOOLS AND LIBRARIES

START YOUR AERO SERIES COLLECTION NOW!

GENERAL DYNAMICS F-111

The latest in the Aero Series General Dynamics F-111 by Jay Miller. Aero Series, Vol. 29. Known to its intimates as the "Aardvark," the F-111 remains perhaps the most controversial warplane of our time. All facets of the F-111's advanced technology are described in detail. This book will be of real value to modelers, aviation buffs and aviation historians.

Great Volumes of this Collection!

A detailed look at many of the world's most famous and noteworthy military aircraft. Each book contains historical commentary, selected photographic material covering all aspects of the aircraft, technical data and specifications, four pages of color drawings in the 52 page volumes and 8 pages of color in the 104 page volumes, plus much more. Provides an unprecedented source of material for the modeler, military enthusiast, collector and historian.

Vols. 1-23 52 pages *(4 pages of color)*

• ENLARGED 104-PAGE SERIES • *(8 pages of color)*

Watch for these forthcoming books in the Aero Series:
F-18 Hornet and XB-70 Valkyrie

AERO
A division of TAB BOOKS Inc.
Blue Ridge Summit, PA 17214